Table of contents

Introduction
A guide to the symbols used in this course book

1.0 Foundations of environmental awareness **3**
Learning outcomes 3

1.1 The meaning of environment, habitats, eco-systems, pollution and sustainability **4**
The environment 4
The weather 5
The climate 5
Habitats 6
Eco-systems 7
Bio-diversity 8
Pollution 9
Sustainability 11
Practice questions 12

1.2 The importance and benefits of sustainable development **13**
Protecting the environment 13
Using natural resources wisely 14
Maintaining stable economic growth 15
Achieving social progress 16
Being competitive 17
Sustainable purchasing 18
Practice questions 20

1.3 Environmental management systems (EMS) **21**
ISO 14001 21
Certification 23
Maintaining the EMS 24
Practice question / References 26

Table of contents

2.0 Pollution, impact assessments and emergencies **27**

2.1 Principles and practice of impact (risk) assessments **28**
Environmental aspects and impacts 28
Cradle-to-grave concept 31
Practice question 34

2.2 The main sources, types, controls and impacts of air pollution **35**
Sources of air pollution 38
Types of air pollution 39
Control of air pollution 41
Effects of air pollution 44
Practice question 48

2.3 The main sources, controls and impacts of water pollution **49**
Sources of water pollution 49
Control of water pollution 54
Effects of water pollution 57
Practice question 60

2.4 The main sources, controls and impacts of environmental noise **61**
Sources of environmental noise 62
Control of environmental noise 63
Impacts of environmental noise 65
Practice question 66

2.5 Types of waste **67**
Practice question 70

2.6 Waste management **71**
The waste hierarchy 75
Managing waste 75
Practice question 80

2.7 Dealing with environmental emergencies **81**
Typical environmental incidents 81
Hazards associated with environmental incidents 82
Emergency response plan 83
Materials and equipment to deal with pollution incidents 84
Training 84
Communications 85
Practice question 87
References 88

Introduction

This course book is designed to provide you with the basic knowledge you need to identify and deal with environmental issues in the workplace, so that you can help to develop a more sustainable workplace. It presents the core information required to achieve the NEBOSH Award in Environmental Awareness at Work, which is the perfect introductory qualification for those who need to be aware of environmental principles as part of their job.

Whether you intend to work through this course book alone or are using it as part of a taught course, you should find that it contains the essential knowledge you need to prepare for the formal NEBOSH assessment. This takes the form of a multiple-choice assessment.

The course book has been structured to match the NEBOSH syllabus, with the information divided into distinct elements, each of which starts with your learning outcomes for that particular section. If you have access to the Internet, we would recommend that you supplement this information by making use of additional resources, e.g. free leaflets and information from the UK Environment Agency (available to download from www.environment-agency.gov.uk) and guidance included on the United Nations Environment Programme website (www.unep.org). Other sources of information are available from the websites given in the References sections.

We are going to cover concepts that are fundamental to environmental awareness at work, such as sustainability, pollution, noise, waste and emergency situations. Throughout the course book we will focus primarily on practical environmental knowledge which will be equally applicable to any type of workplace. As you work through, you will notice that the examples included relate to all sorts of industries, e.g. energy supply, manufacturing, retail and construction. You are also expected to apply the principles you learn to familiar situations in your own workplace.

The course book is intended to be suitable for those working in the UK and international students working all over the world. Environmental management systems, controls and guidance which constitute best practice have been used as the basis, together with international standards and examples. Knowledge of specific legislation, either in the UK or in your own country, is not required and will not be included in the formal assessment.

We recommend that you spend a total of at least 10 hours studying for the NEBOSH Award in Environmental Awareness at Work. Details of how to take the formal assessment can be found on the NEBOSH website www.nebosh.org.uk, where you will also find additional information including a syllabus summary.

A GUIDE TO THE SYMBOLS USED IN THIS COURSE BOOK

ACTIVITY

These ask you to carry out an activity to reinforce what you have just read.

PAUSE FOR THOUGHT

These ask you to think about what you have been learning or to relate it to your own experience.

EXAMPLE

Real or imagined scenarios that give context to points made in the text.

1.0 Foundations of environmental awareness

This element introduces you to key concepts that are fundamental to environmental awareness. You will learn about the components of the natural environment and the potential impact of human activities on them. Then we will consider the idea of sustainability and how organisations can manage their impacts on the environment using environmental management systems.

LEARNING OUTCOMES

On completion of this element, you should be able to:

1.1 Identify the meaning of: the environment; weather; climate; habitats; eco-systems; bio-diversity; pollution; sustainability

1.2 Identify the importance and benefits of sustainable development

1.3 Identify an environmental management system's main components and the certification process

1.1 The meaning of environment, habitats, eco-systems, pollution and sustainability

THE ENVIRONMENT

The environment is everything that surrounds us. This is clearly a very wide description! However, one of the fascinations of studying the environment is the breadth of topics and disciplines that are involved.

Take a moment to write down what makes up the environment around you. Then read on.

To start with, think about things that are very close to you, such as:

- the air you are breathing;
- the room or other space you are occupying;
- the people who are around you; and
- the things you can hear and smell.

Next you need to recognise whether you are in a town or city, or perhaps in the countryside.

- What are the characteristics of the region where you are based?
- What other living things, such as plants and animals, exist around you?

Thinking wider still, you need to be aware that we are all inhabitants of a single planet. Consequently, some of the things that are close to us, e.g. the air we breathe, are part of a global system.

So you can see that 'the environment' encompasses:

- the physical resources of the Earth including air, water, land and raw materials;
- the living resources of animal and plant life; and
- human populations.

It also includes how all of these things relate to each other.

When you consider the environment, you need to think locally, e.g. the immediate surroundings in which your organisation operates; regionally, e.g. the rivers, forests, coastal areas and other eco-systems within your country or continent; and globally, e.g. the oceans/seas which rivers flow into.

1.1 The meaning of environment, habitats, eco-systems, pollution and sustainability

THE WEATHER

Our physical environment is constantly changing and one of the immediate ways in which we experience this is through the weather, but what do we mean by 'the weather'? The weather is all about what is happening to the Earth's atmosphere.

The atmosphere is a thin layer of gases – the 'air' – that surrounds our planet. This layer is really very thin. About 80% of the mass of the atmosphere exists within just 20km of the Earth's surface in a sub-layer called the 'troposphere'. If the Earth was the size of an orange, the troposphere would be no thicker than a layer of cling-film covering the surface of the orange!

Air in the troposphere is warmed by the Sun – but more so over the tropics than the polar regions. This causes differences in air pressure. The weather we experience (cloudy, sunny, rain, calm or stormy) is largely caused by these pressure differences (the 'barometric' pressure).

Air flows from areas of high to low pressure, creating winds. The moisture content of the air changes as these winds blow over oceans, land masses and mountain ranges.

Air moving over warm oceans tends to become more moist. This moisture is likely to be deposited as rain as the air rises over colder land.

The weather is therefore a manifestation of how the atmosphere is behaving at any one time and place. People who study the weather describe this behaviour by measuring variables such as temperature, barometric pressure, moisture content, and wind strength.

THE CLIMATE

If the weather is what we feel at any particular moment, in terms of atmospheric temperature, pressure, rainfall and winds, then the climate is what we experience over a longer period. We expect it to be much wetter and warmer in the tropics than it is in the more temperate areas of Europe and North America. Measurements of weather variables are averaged over periods of 30 years or more. These measurements demonstrate that there are consistent differences in the weather likely to be experienced in different parts of the globe. Different regions are therefore said to have different climates, for example: arctic, temperate, desert, sub-tropical, tropical.

Global climates are generally very stable; however, when measured over millions of years the Earth has undergone some dramatic shifts in climate.

There have been four major ice-ages, the last of which came to an end about 10,000 years ago.

Measurements of the Earth's atmosphere over the last 150 years show that the temperature of the atmosphere has increased by around one degree Celsius. This may not sound much, but might be enough to trigger long-term changes in the weather.

Do you think that the weather is different now from when you were a child?

Such impressions are very subjective. Nevertheless, there is real concern that the atmosphere is being altered by emissions of 'greenhouse gases' such as carbon dioxide which comes from the burning of fossil fuels. Many people think that this is the reason for the global warming that we can measure now. If global warming were to trigger changes in the Earth's climate, this could potentially have very serious consequences.

The major agricultural areas of the Earth might produce less food.

HABITATS

Particular types of animals and plants live in particular localities. These localities provide them with all the physical and biological conditions they need to thrive.

Fish need to live in water. A marine fish, e.g. cod, cannot survive in a freshwater river and is only found in the sea.

So every living thing has a habitat – the place where it lives and where it can usually be found. Factors such as temperature, shelter, moisture, availability of oxygen and presence of food provide good conditions for survival and growth and are essential for a thriving habitat.

The following are examples of animals and their habitats.

- Although the cod is a marine fish, you won't find one in tropical seas, but only in colder northern waters. Here there are abundant smaller fish, squid, mussels and worms on which cod feed.
- Some animals and plants have very restricted habitats, e.g. giant pandas only live in particular forests where there is an abundance of bamboo.

- Brown rats will survive wherever there is some form of shelter and will eat almost anything. They can therefore be found in a wide variety of natural places as well as towns and cities.

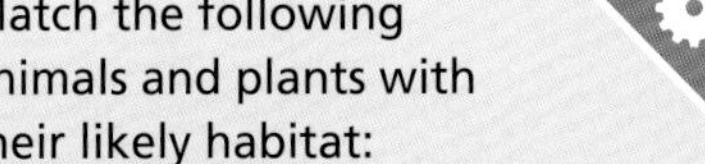

Match the following animals and plants with their likely habitat:

1. Seaweed
2. Blackbird
3. Pine tree
4. Scorpion
5. Heather
6. Bulrush

(a) deciduous woodland
(b) intertidal rocks
(c) hot desert
(d) heath or moorland
(e) pond or lakeside
(f) alpine mountain

Answers are on page 26.

ECO-SYSTEMS

As discussed in the previous section we know that animals and plants can only live where the physical conditions, such as temperature and moisture, suit them. However, animals and plants also affect the physical environment in which they live, so both are inseparable and are inter-related. This relationship between plants, animals, organisms and their physical environment is an 'eco-system'.

Herds of animals, such as zebra, graze on the vast grasslands of Africa. What effects could they have on their environment?

The grasses take moisture and basic nutrients from the soil, and carbon dioxide from the atmosphere. They harness the energy of the Sun to convert these into biological materials (such as carbohydrates) through the process of photosynthesis. The zebra obtain the energy and nutrients they need by eating the grass. They then return nutrients and moisture to the soil through their excreta and when their bodies die and decompose. The animals also spread the seeds of grasses (and other plants) over wide distances. Lions can survive by killing and eating the zebra so they also return nutrients to the soil through their excreta and when they die. So the lives of grasses, zebra and lions are intimately related and energy and materials are cycled between living material, the atmosphere and the soil.

Eco-systems define the interdependency of different plants and animals and the flow of energy and materials between living and non-living components. They have been identified in most natural environments, such as:

- rivers and lakes;
- estuaries;
- forests;
- wetlands;
- Arctic tundra; and
- coral reefs.

BIO-DIVERSITY

There is an enormous variety of wild plants and animals on the Earth. 'Bio-diversity' (a contraction of 'biological diversity') is a concept used to express this variety in terms of the types and numbers of organisms living in a given space.

An area of land, or an eco-system, that contains a high number of different species of animals or plants per unit area, would be described as having a 'high bio-diversity'.

Not all areas of the Earth are equally bio-diverse. Tropical regions tend to have more species in a given area than temperate regions. For example, 40 different species of trees may occur on one hectare of temperate forest in eastern North America, whereas a similar area in lowland Malaysia may support over 550 species[1].

1.1 The meaning of environment, habitats, eco-systems, pollution and sustainability

The contribution that bio-diversity makes to our quality of life is increasingly recognised and valued. The Earth's biological resources are vital to economic and social development by:

- Providing us with sustainable materials for fuel, food and medicines.
- Maintaining the quality of our air, soils, waters and climate.
- Contributing to our health and enjoyment of life.

The UN Convention on Biological Diversity was established in 1992[2], with the aim of co-ordinating international efforts to maintain bio-diversity. Reduction in bio-diversity, especially the extinction of species, is now widely seen as an important measure of the damage caused by human activity and population growth.

POLLUTION

Talk of environmental damage often conjures up images of factory chimneys belching out smoke, or dead fish floating on the surface of a river. Concerns about industrial pollution was one of the reasons for the environmental movement starting but what exactly is pollution? Is it just caused by industrial activities?

Look at the photograph of the dead fish on the beach. Why do you think the fish has died?

Pollution is usually taken to mean the presence of contamination in the environment, which has the potential to cause adverse effects on the natural environment or on life.

In this case it seems quite likely that some contaminant has been deposited in the sea, and that this has had an adverse effect by poisoning the fish. This could be a harmful chemical or rubbish of a toxic nature.

Environmental pollution usually involves the following factors:

1. A source of contaminant

This might be a physical substance or a chemical, or perhaps a form of energy such as heat, noise or light.

2. A target (or receptor)

This is something that the contaminant may come into contact with, such as:

- wild animals and plants;
- human populations;
- eco-systems (e.g. rivers, estuaries, forests, seas);
- global systems (e.g. the atmosphere).

3. An impact

This is the adverse effect that the contaminant has on a target or receptor. In the example above, the contaminant has killed the fish.

When a contaminant is released into the environment, we also need to recognise that the impact may be local or global.

The smoky emissions from a power-station chimney might have a local impact on nearby residents (by affecting their breathing). However, the emissions will also contain carbon dioxide (one of the main greenhouse gases) and this has the potential to affect the global climate through global warming. (This is covered in more detail in Element 2.)

Outside of the heavy industrial and utilities sectors, comparatively few organisations operate processes that involve large-scale emissions or discharges of contaminants into the environment.

The meaning of environment, habitats, eco-systems, pollution and sustainability

Do you think your organisation is causing pollution?

Are you as an individual causing pollution?

Cars: exhaust fumes from road vehicles is one of the greatest sources of air pollution in towns and villages.

Electricity use: we are not ***directly*** responsible for the emissions from

the power stations that provide our electricity. We do though have some ***indirect*** responsibility because of our demand for electricity.

What sources of environmental pollution do you think your organisation is responsible for?

Write these down, distinguishing between those sources that the organisation is ***directly*** responsible for and those where it has some ***indirect*** responsibility.

SUSTAINABILITY

The natural environment provides the things we need to live healthy and productive lives, including water to drink, air to breathe, food to eat and raw materials for manufacturing.

This means that environmental protection needs to be an integral part of social and economic development, as we strive to become wealthier. If we damage the environment or deplete stocks of natural resources in the process, future generations will find it harder to maintain the same standard of life that we currently enjoy.

Practice Questions

We are entitled to be healthy and prosperous, but we need to achieve this in a sustainable way that does not irretrievably damage the natural capital of the Earth. In 1992, the UN held a landmark summit meeting at which the concept of sustainable development was first widely discussed. Following the summit, the UN Rio Declaration on Environment and Development[3] was issued. The meaning of sustainable development was enshrined in Principle 3 of the Declaration:

"The right to development must be fulfilled so as to equitably meet developmental and environmental needs of present and future generations".

The importance and benefits of sustainable development are covered in more depth in section 1.2.

PRACTICE QUESTIONS

Q1 Bio-diversity is a concept used to

A reduce pollution.

B describe the types and numbers of wild plants and animals living in a given space.

C place a monetary value on wildlife.

D save energy.

Q2 Pollution is

A anything that affects the environment.

B only caused by heavy industries.

C the presence of contamination with the potential to cause adverse effects on the natural environment or on life.

D using too much energy.

1.2 The importance and benefits of sustainable development

What do you think 'sustainability' means for your organisation?

Write down some bullet points and review them after you have read this section.

Sustainable development is a concept that is often referred to, but not always understood. 'Sustainability' is not just a theoretical idea; it may help an organisation both to develop itself and to contribute to global progress.

The idea of sustainable development was born out of the growing realisation that our way of life has become inherently 'unsustainable'. Environmental issues were the first to set alarm bells ringing as we saw increasing loss of forests and wilderness areas, more animals and plants facing extinction and fish stocks declining. Devastating famines in Africa, fuel shortages accompanied by steeply rising prices, and the threat to the world's climate from global warming have since reinforced the belief that we are taking more from the Earth than it can bear.

We know that this situation cannot continue forever. If we carry on as we are, we - or our children - will eventually find ourselves short of land, wild places, wild animals and plants, food, fuel and other resources.

If we just stand back and let this happen, the consequences for our quality of life will be dramatic. We need to take action to bring our economies back into line with the capacity of the planet - this is what sustainable development is all about.

At the ground-breaking UN Rio Earth Summit in 1992, sustainable development was defined as follows:

"the right to development must be fulfilled so as to equitably meet developmental and environmental needs of present and future generations".

Think for a moment about what this might mean.
What are our present needs and how do we recognise the needs of future generations?

To answer these questions we need to think about several different, but related areas.

PROTECTING THE ENVIRONMENT

Our natural environment provides us with drinking water, air to breathe, land to grow food, mineral resources, space and pleasant surroundings in which to live. Protecting the environment is therefore central to sustainable development.

This means that we need to:

- protect rivers, lakes and groundwater from pollution;
- reduce pollution of the atmosphere - especially emissions of the greenhouse gases that contribute to global warming;
- maintain the diversity of wild animals and plants;
- avoid using agricultural chemicals that can harm wildlife.

USING NATURAL RESOURCES WISELY

Mankind has known for a long time that naturally renewable resources – such as stocks of fish in the sea, or timber in forests – can be managed so that they produce a ***sustainable yield***. This means that we can regularly harvest a proportion of the resource, and that proportion will be replaced by natural growth, so that stocks are maintained indefinitely. However, modern fishing methods and indiscriminate clearing of forests for the growth of crops far exceed the capacity for natural regeneration. Our renewable resources have been in serious decline.

Many of the resources we depend on are non-renewable. Using these in a sustainable way is even more of a challenge.

1.2 The importance and benefits of sustainable development

World Oil Consumption, 1950 – 2004 (Million Tons)

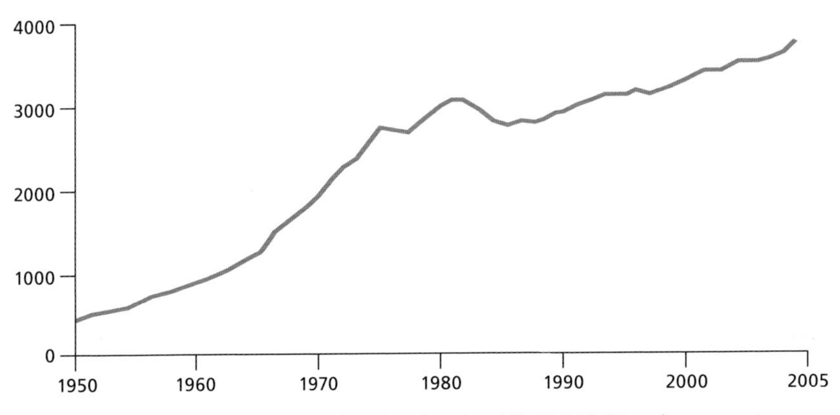

Source: adapted from Worldwatch Institute based on UN, BP, DOE, IEA and press reports

Oil is a non-renewable resource that we depend on heavily – not just for use as fuel, but also because many materials such as plastics are made from oil. We know that oil supplies are finite and that we need to use less by:

- Being more efficient in our use of oil-based resources.
- Finding renewable alternatives.
- Recycling oil-based materials such as plastics wherever possible.

Make a note of all the opportunities that you can think of for your organisation to use less oil. In other words, what oil-based materials could you:

- Use less?
- Substitute with more sustainable materials?
- Recycle?

MAINTAINING STABLE ECONOMIC GROWTH

Economic growth is important to our well-being. We want to be prosperous enough to provide for our basic needs and also to enjoy life. How do we ensure that future generations can also enjoy stable economic growth?

This is one of the most difficult, and controversial, questions that sustainable development poses.

- Some people maintain that economic growth and sustainability are incompatible – because growth implies that we simply consume more and more resources.
- Others suggest that we need to re-define what we mean by economic growth and move away from the idea that growth can only be defined by an increase in monetary Gross Domestic Product (GDP).

The key to moving towards a more sustainable economy may be to change our lifestyle to one:

- which consumes fewer resources;
- where we actually have less money, but stronger communities and less stressful lifestyles;
- where there is less inequality between richer and poorer members of society.

Considering all that we've said above, what do you think about sustainability?

ACHIEVING SOCIAL PROGRESS

It is widely recognised that the needs of present and future generations cannot be expressed only in environmental and economic terms - the concept of sustainable development should also embrace social well-being. Specific social goals and objectives are now being integrated with environmental and economic issues in sustainability programmes. In the UK, for example, it has been proposed that measures of sustainability[4] should include issues such as:

- life expectancy;
- poverty;
- long-term unemployment;
- social mobility; and
- housing provision.

This idea has an international dimension. Trade is increasingly global and there is a danger that prosperity and well-being in the developed world is being achieved at the expense of workers in less developed countries. We need to make sure that international trade is fair and ethical, and promotes social goals in the developing world. Many organisations are now taking steps to ensure that:

- the goods they buy are not produced with child labour;
- workers receive fair wages and enjoy reasonable and safe working conditions.

1.2 The importance and benefits of sustainable development

What items does your organisation purchase that are likely to have been made in developing countries?

BEING COMPETITIVE

Organisations pursue a sustainable development path because they want to do the right thing and to be responsible citizens. Being responsible and accountable can also make your organisation more competitive and bring significant commercial advantages. The social landscape in which organisations and business operate has changed. Concerns about environmental protection and ethical trade are now commonplace. Your organisation needs to respond accordingly, for example:

- Investors increasingly use corporate responsibility performance measures to help them pick well-run companies. In fact, we've seen the rise of a distinct class of investors – the Socially Responsible Investment (SRI) funds that specialise in investing in ethically sound companies. It is claimed that SRI funds now account for around 10-15% of total investment funds under management in London.
- Customers have shown that they care about environmental and fair trade issues and will support initiatives such as the Forest Stewardship Council (FSC) that promotes goods made from wood that comes from sustainable forests.

This means that organisations which pursue a well-considered sustainability strategy can benefit through:

- lower operating costs, e.g. through increased energy efficiency and by reducing waste production and water usage;
- better access to capital;
- enhanced reputation and improved sales with customers who want to know that what they buy has been produced in an environmentally and socially responsible way.

B&Q is the largest home improvement retailer in the UK, with around 350 stores and a £3-4 billion per year turnover. In the early 1990s, B&Q was targeted by pressure groups and a national newspaper campaign. The company was accused of being connected with the destruction of tropical rainforests – through selling products such as garden furniture and front doors that were made of tropical hardwood.

At the time, B&Q had no answers to these concerns – but they did realise that their customers cared about forest destruction and that they needed to take action. That was the start of a 20-year journey to find out exactly where their timber was coming from and to ensure that it was all responsibly sourced from well-managed forests. Along the way, B&Q became a founding partner of the FSC (Forest Stewardship Council), the first organisation in the world to provide a credible scheme for certifying supplies of well-managed, sustainable timber.

At the outset many people doubted that the company could meet its ambitious target to only supply responsibly sourced wood, while at the same time maintaining competitive prices.

B&Q has proved the doubters wrong – the company has enhanced its reputation by making a major contribution to forest protection. It has also maintained its number one position in the marketplace.

SUSTAINABLE PURCHASING

Achieving sustainable development needs to involve radical changes in the way goods and services are supplied. One of the ways your organisation can make a difference is through the purchasing choices that they make.

The initial price you pay for an item is important of course, but a more sustainable approach is to consider the cost of the product throughout its life cycle.

Energy conservation is a good example of how you can achieve a win-win situation, by helping the environment while also saving yourself some money. In fact, many organisations now operate sustainable purchasing programmes that cover all of their major purchases of goods and services.

1.2 The importance and benefits of sustainable development

Organisations can demonstrate savings and benefits across a range of factors including:

- cost;
- reduced waste and improved resource efficiency;
- security of supply (e.g. by avoiding supplies of products that contain banned or dangerous substances).

Sustainable purchasing programmes also help to stimulate markets for environmentally and ethically sound products.

The use phase of a washing machine accounts for over 95% of the energy consumed during its life cycle. Who pays for this energy? You do of course! So it may make sense to pay a little more for a model that is more energy-efficient. You could save a lot more money in the long run. The environment could benefit too in terms of conserving fuel resources and reducing greenhouse gas emissions. The same argument applies to cars and most other energy-intensive equipment.

Go back to the points that you wrote down at the beginning of this section.

Have your thoughts on the meaning of 'sustainability' for your organisation changed at all?

Practice Questions

PRACTICE QUESTIONS

Q3 Which best describes the benefits to an organisation of pursuing a sound sustainability strategy?

A Being able to buy goods more cheaply from developing countries.

B Paying less tax.

C Enhancing their reputation with environmentally and socially aware customers.

D Reducing their employment costs.

Q4 Which best describes sustainable development?

A Ensuring all our needs and wants are met providing it leaves something for the future.

B Making sure we can provide everything the current population needs.

C Equitably meeting developmental and environmental needs of present and future generations.

D Stopping any activity now that harms the environment.

1.3 Environmental management systems (EMS)

Many organisations find it difficult to make a start in managing their environmental responsibilities. You will have realised by now that any organisation can have many different interactions with the environment. Deciding which issues should have priority, and exactly what should be done, is not always easy.

Environmental management systems have been developed to help organisations manage their environmental issues systematically and comprehensively. The environmental management system (EMS) model set out in the international ISO 14001 standard[5] is now the most widely accepted.

Organisations that follow this standard can benefit by:

- Managing their environmental impacts in the most resource-efficient way to bring about improvements.
- Making cost savings through better control of issues such as energy consumption and waste management.
- Achieving compliance with environmental legislation.
- Demonstrating their environmental commitment to suppliers and other interested parties such as regulatory authorities, insurance companies, shareholders and local residents.

ISO 14001

The EMS model incorporated in the ISO 14001 standard is based on the simple idea of plan-do-check-act. In an environmental context, this means:

1. ***Identifying*** the environmental impacts associated with an organisation's activities.
2. Deciding exactly what ***action*** is going to be taken in relation to each of those impacts.
3. At intervals checking (or ***auditing***) that the actions specified have been carried out.
4. Periodically ***reviewing*** the EMS to make sure it is working effectively and to take account of any changes affecting the organisation, and ensuring that the organisation is continually improving its environmental performance.

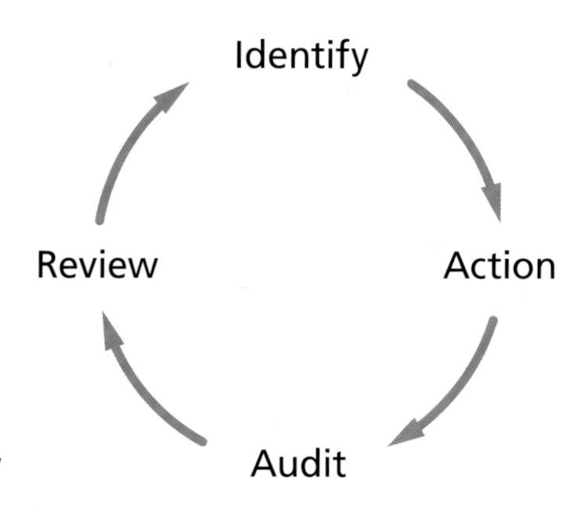

The requirements of the ISO 14001 standard are consistent with this basic approach:

ISO 14001 component	Key tasks
Environmental policy	Define an environmental policy. This should set out the organisation's priorities and reflect top management's commitment to improvement and to achieving legal compliance.
Planning	Identify the environmental issues and potential impacts associated with the organisation's activities, products and services. Identify any legal requirements that apply to these issues. Set objectives and targets to bring about improvements where possible.
Implementation and operation	Ensure that the organisation has processes, policies and procedures in place and that roles and responsibilities for maintaining and operating the EMS are defined. Ensure that there are adequate resources. Identify training needs for members of the organisation. Ensure that day-to-day controls over operations that have the potential to cause environmental impacts are in place.
Checking	Monitor performance, e.g. in achieving the objectives and targets. Undertake measurements where necessary to demonstrate legal compliance, e.g. regarding the requirements of environmental permits. Undertake audits of the system at planned intervals, to determine whether EMS system procedures are being followed.
Management review	Top management must periodically review the performance of the system to make sure that the EMS continues to be effective. If the organisation's activities change, or there are any new legal requirements, the EMS must be adapted accordingly.

CERTIFICATION

A key benefit of developing and maintaining an EMS that conforms to the international standard ISO 14001 is that it can be independently audited by an accredited certification body. If the EMS is found to meet the requirements of the standard, the organisation concerned is awarded a certificate endorsed by the relevant national authority.

Certified organisations may display the certificate in their premises, and also show an approved certification logo on their signage, letterheads and advertising material. This constitutes proof that they have in place an effective ISO 14001 EMS. There may be considerable commercial benefit in obtaining formal certification. Many companies and other organisations now require ISO 14001 certification from suppliers as a condition of doing business.

Certification will involve auditors from the certification body reviewing EMS documentation. They will also undertake site inspections and interviews with workers who have a role in implementing the EMS.

Organisations seeking certification for the first time generally go through a two-stage audit process:

Stage 1 audit

This is based on a detailed document review. The auditors will:

- Assess whether all the various elements of the standard have been covered by the EMS procedures.
- Assess whether all the significant environmental issues have been addressed.
- Make a brief tour of the organisation's main site and hold discussions with a limited number of key workers.
- Identify any major deficiencies (non-conformances) and raise these with senior management. The deficiencies must be addressed before proceeding to Stage 2.

Stage 2 audit

This is a more in-depth audit. The EMS procedures will be extensively sampled and implementation tested through a combination of document review and interviews with a wide range of workers. If appropriate, auditors may visit other sites that the organisation operates.

Organisations that pass the Stage 2 audit are usually awarded certification for a three-year period. During this period they must undergo surveillance audits, usually every six months. At the end of the three-year period, an organisation must apply for re-certification.

MAINTAINING THE EMS

A successful and certified EMS needs constant maintenance to ensure that it continues to meet the requirements of the standard and reflects changing circumstances. ISO 14001 requires that internal audits are undertaken at planned intervals to make sure that established procedures are being consistently followed. At regular intervals, senior management must also review the performance of the EMS to ensure that it remains effective and has kept pace with changing circumstances.

The activities of the organisation might change, e.g. as it expands or diversifies into new areas and employs new workers.

New activities may involve different environmental impacts. These need to be examined to determine whether any changes should be made to the EMS, such as:

- Strengthening day-to-day controls on activities that can affect the environment.
- Setting revised improvement objectives and targets.
- Undertaking additional measurements to track performance.
- Expanding worker training.

External circumstances may also change.

Legislation may change or new legislation may be introduced that places new requirements on the organisation.

1.3 Environmental management systems (EMS)

An important element of maintaining an EMS is to follow developments in legislation very closely and ensure that legal compliance is maintained.

Certain individuals within an organisation will have specially designated roles for maintaining the EMS.

- ISO 14001 requires the designation of a management representative with overall responsibility for co-ordinating the maintenance of the EMS.
- Top management are expected to provide commitment and resources and to lead the regular reviews of the performance of the EMS.
- Other individuals may be given specific tasks to ensure that particular procedures are carried out or targets met.

An important principle underlying any EMS is that all of an organisation's workers have some role to play in maintaining the system. They must all be aware of the organisation's environmental policy, objectives and targets and follow EMS procedures covering activities that they are involved in.

If there is a procedure for segregating waste, all workers must follow this.

Certification auditors will test worker awareness and use this as a key measure of the adequacy of the EMS.

Practice Question / References

PRACTICE QUESTION

Q5 The ISO 14001 environmental management system standard is based on a simple idea. Which best describes the ISO 14001 approach?

A Plan-Do-Check-Act.

B Complying with environmental legislation.

C Meeting the needs of the current generation without compromising the ability of future generations to meet their own needs.

D Reducing pollution.

ANSWER TO HABITATS ACTIVITY

1. (b)
2. (a)
3. (f)
4. (c)
5. (d)
6. (e)

REFERENCES

1 The World Environment 1972-1992, UNEP, 1992

2 http://www.cbd.int/intro/default.shtml

3 http://www.un.org/documents/ga/conf151/aconf15126-1annex1.htm

4 http://data.gov.uk/dataset/sustainable_development_indicators_in_your_pocket

5 EN ISO 14001:2004, Environmental management systems – Requirements with guidance for use, European Committee for Standardisation, Brussels

2.0 Pollution, impact assessments and emergencies

In this element we are going to look in more depth at the sources of environmental pollution and the measures that are available to bring about improvements to the environment. You will learn how the environmental issues associated with any organisation can be identified and characterised.

On completion of this element, you should be able to:

- 2.1 Outline the principles and practice of impact (risk) assessments
- 2.2 Identify the main sources, types, controls and impacts of air pollution
- 2.3 Identify the main sources, controls and impacts of water pollution
- 2.4 Identify the main sources, controls and impacts of environmental noise
- 2.5 Identify waste types
- 2.6 Identify the waste hierarchy and ways to effectively manage waste
- 2.7 Outline the measures that need to be in place when dealing with emergencies

2.1 Principles and practice of impact (risk) assessments

'What environmental impacts do we have?'

That's the question all organisations need to answer, before they can start to think about developing an environmental improvement programme. If you don't know what the problems are, you can't fix them!

There are tools and techniques that organisations can use to identify the environmental issues associated with their activities. This needs to be done systematically to ensure that:

- nothing significant is omitted; and
- managing the most important issues is given priority.

ENVIRONMENTAL ASPECTS AND IMPACTS

This photograph shows a coal-fired power station.

What effects do you think the power station might be having on the environment?

We can see that the chimney is emitting some smoke and fumes into the surrounding air. This is clearly one way in which the facility is interacting with the environment – this is an 'environmental aspect'.

The international environmental management system standard ISO 14001 defines an ***environmental aspect*** as an:

'element of an organisation's activities or products or services that can interact with the environment'.

2.1 Principles and practice of impact (risk) assessments

One environmental aspect of the power station's activities is the emission of exhaust gases from its chimney into the atmosphere. But why does this matter? What is the environmental damage, or impact, caused?

There is a very useful model that you can use to identify and characterise environmental impacts in these types of situation. It has the following elements:

Source
Is there a source of contamination? This might be a toxic chemical, a physical substance, or energy in the form of heat, noise or light.

Receptor
Is there something that can be harmed or damaged by this source of contamination? This might be:

- wild animals or plants;
- human populations;
- eco-systems (e.g. rivers, estuaries, forests, seas);
- global systems (e.g. the climate) or natural resources.

Pathway
Is there a route by which the contamination can reach a receptor? This could be drainage systems taking contaminated agricultural run-off water to watercourses.

If we can make the link: ***source – pathway – receptor*** then we have an impact.

ISO 14001 defines an ***environmental impact*** as:

'any change to the environment, whether adverse or beneficial, wholly or partially resulting from an organisation's environmental aspects'.

Can you apply the source-pathway-receptor model to any of your organisation's activities?

If we apply the source-pathway-receptor model to the emission of exhaust gases from the power-station chimney, we will find that this one aspect can potentially have a number of quite different impacts.

Local residents could be affected by smoke and grit, which passes up the chimney and into the local atmosphere and is then deposited over the surrounding land. The smoke could be a nuisance, e.g. dirty deposits on washing and cars, or people might suffer health effects if they are susceptible to breathing problems, e.g. due to asthma or bronchitis.

SOURCE	PATHWAY	RECEPTOR	IMPACT
Smoke and grit from coal-fired boiler	Released via chimney into the atmosphere. Deposited on the ground.	Local residents	*Nuisance:* Dirty washing *Health:* Asthma

There will also be other sources of contamination (besides smoke and grit) in emissions of exhaust gases from the power-station chimney.

One of the main components of the power-station exhaust is carbon dioxide. This is one of the main greenhouse gases and contributes to global warming and climate change.

Another important component of the exhaust is sulphur dioxide. If this gas gets into the atmosphere it can be transported many hundreds of miles away by the prevailing wind.

Sulphur dioxide from power stations in the UK is often detected over Scandinavian countries.

Sulphur dioxide can react with moisture in the atmosphere to create 'acid rain'. This has been shown to be damaging forests and lakes in countries such as Norway and Sweden.

So the emission of exhaust gases from the power station's chimney into the atmosphere - a single aspect - is potentially having a number of different environmental impacts which involve different contaminants, pathways and receptors:

2.1 Principles and practice of impact (risk) assessments

Source (Contaminant)	Pathway	Receptor	Impact
Smoke and grit particles	Chimney to local atmosphere Deposited over surrounding land	Local residents	Dirty washing
Smoke and grit particles	Chimney to local atmosphere	Local residents	Respiratory problems
Sulphur dioxide	Chimney to atmosphere Deposited as acid rain over Scandinavia	Norwegian salmon	Declining fish stocks
Sulphur dioxide	Chimney to atmosphere Deposited as acid rain over Scandinavia	Norwegian trees	Forest die-back
Carbon dioxide	Chimney to global atmosphere	Global atmosphere	Climate change

What environmental impacts do you think your organisation has?

Write down some ideas – we will come back to them later.

CRADLE-TO-GRAVE CONCEPT

The ***source-pathway-receptor*** model is very useful in situations where an organisation is releasing contaminants into the environment from its own activities, such as:

- exhaust emissions from a boiler; or
- discharges of liquid effluent from a manufacturing process.

These are examples of ***direct*** environmental aspects, where the organisation clearly has management control and responsibility.

However, many organisations (especially in the service sector) may not operate equipment or processes that release contaminants directly into the environment.

Does this mean that such organisations have no environmental aspects or impacts?

What do you think?

Consider the power station. Who is responsible for managing the environmental impacts that we identified? Clearly the operator of the power station has the main responsibility – but what about organisations that use the electricity it generates?

We create a demand for electricity, and the more electricity we use, the more emissions the power station makes. So it is fair to say that:

- our consumption of electricity is an ***indirect*** environmental aspect; and
- we have some capacity to reduce the associated environmental impacts, mainly by using less electricity.

An approach that is particularly useful for analysing indirect environmental aspects is ***life-cycle analysis***. This is often referred to as the ***cradle-to-grave*** approach and involves looking at the environmental aspects of products and services upstream and downstream of an organisation's activities.

Consider the life cycle of a typical domestic appliance, e.g. a washing machine. The starting point, or 'cradle', is the extraction and production of raw materials that are used to make it (such as steel, plastic and paint). These materials need to be transported to the manufacturer, who makes the washing machine and then distributes it to the customer. The customer will use the machine for many years, before it comes to the end of its useful life and needs to be disposed of (the 'grave').

At each stage in this life cycle we can identify:

- Inputs: the raw materials and energy that are consumed.
- Outputs: in terms of emissions and wastes that are generated which can have an environmental impact.

2.1 Principles and practice of impact (risk) assessments

1 Extraction and production of raw materials such as steel and plastic

INPUTS	OUTPUTS
Iron-ore mining; Steel production	Habitat degradation; Dust and sulphur oxide emissions; Water pollution (suspended solids)

2. Transport of raw materials to the manufacturer

INPUTS	OUTPUTS
Use of lorries, rail wagons, ships; Fuel consumption	Engine emissions

3. Manufacture of the washing machine

INPUTS	OUTPUTS
Use of heavy machinery; Consumption of fuel and electricity; Consumption of steel and plastic	Wastes (steel, plastic, oil); Air emissions (dust)

4. Distribution to the customer

INPUTS	OUTPUTS
Use of road transport; Use of warehousing and shop premises; Consumption of electricity and fuel	Engine and power-station emissions

5. Use by the customer

INPUTS	OUTPUTS
Consumption of water; Consumption of electricity; Consumption of detergents	Power-station emissions; Waste water

6. Disposal of the washing machine at the end of its useful life

INPUTS	OUTPUTS
Use of road transport; Use of breaking machinery; Use of landfill space; Consumption of electricity and fuel	Land degradation; Engine and power-station emissions

Look at the diagram above. Which stage(s) in the life cycle of a washing machine do you think are associated with the greatest environmental impacts?

Analysis of inputs and outputs shows that the environmental 'hot spots' in the life cycle are stage 1 (extraction and production of raw materials) and stage 5 (customer use). Therefore, washing-machine manufacturers who want to reduce their environmental impacts:

- must manage the ***direct*** environmental impacts associated with their own activities when they make the washing machines (stage 3); and
- should try to influence the ***indirect*** environmental impacts, upstream and downstream, in the product life-cycle.

They might take the following actions:

Stage 1: Extraction of raw materials
Reduce raw material consumption through good product design and efficient manufacturing.

Only purchase materials from suppliers that have environmental management systems certified to ISO 14001.

Stage 5: Customer use
Design washing machines that use as little energy and water as possible for each wash.

Using what you have learnt about life-cycle analysis, identify the stages in the life cycle of a plastic carrier bag, including the inputs and outputs at each stage.

PRACTICE QUESTION

Q1 Which would constitute an environmental aspect?

A Car exhaust emissions.

B Ozone depletion.

C Acid rain.

D Dead fish in a river.

2.2 The main sources, types, controls and impacts of air pollution

Pollution of the air we breathe has been a problem for centuries, as cities have grown larger and human society has become more industrialised. Burning of coal for domestic heating and cooking and the development of metal furnaces and chemical works, led to air pollution becoming a major public health issue in industrialised countries during the 19th century. Today, progress has been made in controlling air pollution, but air quality is still declining around the world, especially in large cities with high numbers of road vehicles.

SOURCES OF AIR POLLUTION

Energy consumption

Population growth brings increased consumption of goods and services and greater industrialisation leading to higher energy consumption. As most of the world's energy still comes from burning fossil fuels, increased energy consumption usually leads to greater air pollution.

Write down as many types of fossil fuel as you can think of.

What fossil fuels does your organisation use?

Fossil fuels

Have you ever wondered why fuels such as coal, oil and gas are called 'fossil' fuels? It is because they are all derived from plants that died many millions of years ago and became fossilised deep beneath the surface of the Earth.

Most of the coal we use comes from the remains of trees and ferns that grew in vast, swampy forests around 300 million years ago. As this vegetation died, it sank to the bottom of the swamps and was slowly transformed by pressure from the build-up of layers of sediment, so that the carbon contained within the vegetation was compressed into coal. Natural gas (methane) and crude oil (petroleum) were produced in a similar way from the remains of dead marine plants. The most common fossil fuels are shown in the table opposite.

Fuel	Description
Coal	Solid, black carbon-based mineral. The largest source of fuel for electricity generation worldwide.
Anthracite	Very high quality coal, with a carbon content >90%.
Lignite	Low quality 'brown coal', with a carbon content 60-70%.
Coke	Solid residue made by heating coal in the absence of air. Widely used in steel furnaces.
Petrol / Gasoline	Mixture of hydrocarbon compounds distilled from petroleum (crude oil) and containing various additives. The most common fuel for passenger road vehicles and aircraft.
Diesel / DERV	Mixture of hydrocarbon compounds distilled from petroleum but more dense than petrol. The most common fuel for freight road vehicles. Sometimes used to fuel boilers for space heating. (Note that biodiesel is not a fossil fuel.)
Fuel oil / Heating oil / Paraffin	Mixtures of hydrocarbon compounds distilled from petroleum. Available in various grades. Used to fuel domestic and industrial boilers and ships.
Natural gas	Naturally occurring hydrocarbon gas mostly consisting of methane. Widely used for domestic and industrial heating and electricity generation.
LNG (Liquefied Natural Gas)	Natural gas condensed to a liquid for bulk transport by refrigerating to -162°C Converted back to gas before use as above.
LPG (Liquefied Petroleum Gas)	Propane or butane (or a mixture). Used as a fuel in heating appliances, cookers and sometimes road vehicles.

2.2 The main sources, types, controls and impacts of air pollution

All fossil fuels have a very high carbon content, which combines chemically with oxygen in the atmosphere when they are burned. Getting energy from fossil fuels releases:

- large quantities of carbon dioxide into the atmosphere (carbon dioxide is one of the main greenhouse gases contributing to climate change); and
- a substantial amount of energy in the form of heat and light.

A range of other contaminants may also be released into the atmosphere, depending on the exact composition of the fossil fuel used and the presence of additives and impurities. The main contaminants likely to be released are:

Contaminant	Description
Carbon dioxide	One of the main greenhouse gases which contributes to climate change.
Sulphur oxides (SOx)	Contributes to the formation of acid rain.
Nitrogen oxides (NOx)	Contributes to the formation of acid rain and city smog.
Particulates	Small particles of soot and ash that may cause respiratory problems.

In addition, much smaller quantities of highly toxic materials may be released including:

- compounds of lead and mercury; and
- some radioactive substances.

The presence of these toxins depends on the exact source of the fuel and any additives that may have been used.

Lead compounds used to be added to petrol to help combustion in car engines.

Fossil fuels account for over 85% of the world's energy consumption[1]. So it is not hard to see that burning them - to generate electricity, run transport, heat offices and homes, and provide power for industrial processes - is the root cause of much of the world's air pollution.

World Energy Consumption by Sector

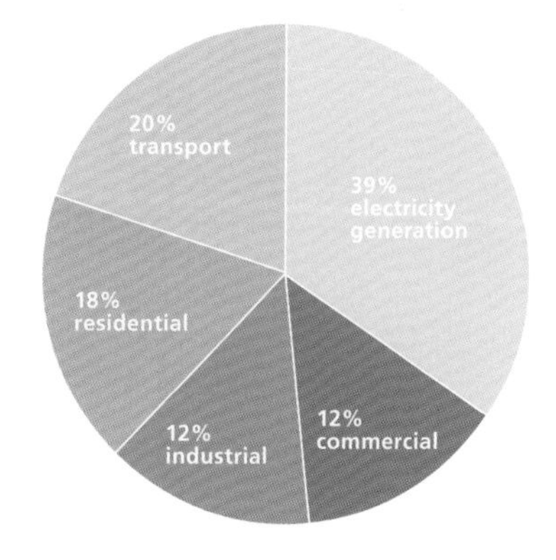

Data sourced from US Energy Information Administration

Industrial processes

All industrial activities contribute to air pollution by using fossil fuels as a source of energy. However, certain industries also emit pollutants into the atmosphere due to the nature of the processes that they operate. The main industrial sources of air pollutants are:

Industry	Air pollutants
Oil and gas refining	Particulates, Sulphur oxides (SOx), Nitrogen oxides (NOx), Volatile Organic Compounds (solvent fumes), Benzene, Hydrogen sulphide, Hydrogen fluoride.
Cement manufacturing	Particulates, Carbon dioxide, Sulphur oxides (SOx), Nitrogen oxides (NOx), Hydrogen chloride, Benzene, Toluene, Xylene.
Metal smelting and refining	Particulates, Carbon dioxide, Sulphur oxides (SOx), Nitrogen oxides (NOx), Hydrocarbons, Acid gases.
Pulp and paper manufacture	Particulates, Volatile Organic Compounds (solvent fumes), Chloroform, Formaldehyde, Ammonia.
Chemical production	Volatile Organic Compounds (solvent fumes), Acid gases.
Waste incineration	Particulates, Carbon dioxide, Sulphur oxides (SOx), Nitrogen oxides (NOx), Hydrogen chloride, Hydrogen fluoride.

2.2 The main sources, types, controls and impacts of air pollution

TYPES OF AIR POLLUTION

Contaminants that are released into the atmosphere may exist in a number of different physical forms:

Particulates	This is the general term for contaminants that exist as small solid particles. It includes: • **Smoke** Consists mostly of bits of carbon that are between 0.1 and 10 microns in size. • **Dust** Any size of solid particle that is suspended in the air. (This term is sometimes used interchangeably with 'particulate'.) • **Grit** Larger, solid particles that are greater than 75 microns. Grit will often be deposited from the atmosphere onto the ground quite readily. • **Fume** Particles that are so small (less than 1 micron across) that they often appear to the eye as a hazy vapour. • **Fibre** Particles that have an elongated shape. Some fibre particles are very dangerous, e.g. asbestos fibres, because they can damage the internal surface of the lungs if inhaled, causing inflammation and possibly cancer.
Gases	Substances that exist in the gas phase at everyday temperatures and pressures, e.g. carbon dioxide, nitrogen and sulphur dioxide. Gases are compressible and can fill the whole of any container. They become liquefied at extremely low temperatures or high pressure.
Vapours	Substances in the gas phase, but which are normally liquids at everyday temperatures and pressures. Vapours will often condense back to the liquid phase very easily - water vapour is the most common example.
Mist	Fine liquid droplets suspended in the atmosphere, e.g. when you use a fly spray.

The term ***odour*** is also frequently used in relation to types of air pollution. This describes the offensive smell that many air pollutants can cause, rather than their physical form. Any of the forms of contaminant described previously could potentially create an odour.

Pollutants may be released deliberately into the atmosphere, e.g. via a chimney. They may also be emitted accidentally, e.g. via leaks in pipework or when a volatile liquid is being decanted (think about the petrol vapour you can smell as you fill up your car). These unplanned releases are known as ***fugitive emissions***.

In 1984, a Union Carbide Corporation factory manufacturing pesticides in Bhopal in India leaked around 30 tonnes of toxic gas into the atmosphere. The leak was caused by a process failure when water accidentally penetrated a tank holding the toxic chemical, methyl isocyanate. The resulting chemical reaction caused the temperature and pressure in the tank to rise dramatically and toxic gas was vented through a pressure relief valve.

The toxic gas drifted over local residential areas, causing death and serious injuries. Estimates vary, but it is thought that around 8,000 people died and over 30,000 suffered severe injuries within weeks of the incident occurring[2].

The main sources, types, controls and impacts of air pollution

CONTROL OF AIR POLLUTION

Controlling air pollution is an environmental priority. What is the best way of achieving this? There are different answers for different situations but generally a hierarchy of controls applies based on the effectiveness of these controls.

MOST EFFECTIVE

ELIMINATE

MINIMISE

RENDER HARMLESS

The best way to control an emission is to prevent it happening at all. If we can ***eliminate*** the source of a contaminant from our process or activity, then that contaminant can't be released to the atmosphere.

During the 1970s there was growing concern that the health of children in urban areas was being affected by elevated levels of lead. The source of the lead was a substance (tetraethyl lead) added to petrol to improve vehicle performance, which resulted in lead being emitted from car exhausts. New engine designs and changes to fuel formulations removed the need for lead additives and, by the year 2000, the use of lead in petrol had been banned in most countries of the world. So, we stopped using lead in petrol and eliminated emissions of lead from car exhausts – problem solved!

Garden sheds and fences have traditionally been painted with creosote to preserve them and make them look good. Applying creosote results in volatile and potentially toxic substances being released into the surrounding air, so manufacturers have now come up with water-based alternatives to creosote. These can be made in bright colours, creating the opportunity for more attractive gardens in addition to eliminating the source of pollution.

It is not always possible to eliminate the source of a contaminant completely, so the next best thing is to ***minimise*** emissions. We have seen the relationship between air pollution and burning fossil fuels. Every opportunity we take to use less energy not only saves money, but also reduces the air emissions from burning fossil fuels.

Think of a car – an obvious way to save energy and reduce emissions is to use it less. Riding a bicycle to the shops might be an alternative.

Over the longer term, lasting improvements in the fuel efficiency of cars have been achieved through research and development by the motor industry.

We saw earlier that burning coal in power stations can result in emissions of sulphur dioxide, a significant source of acid rain that can damage forests and lakes. The power companies have taken an important step to minimise emissions. They have switched to burning low-sulphur coal, which produces significantly less sulphur dioxide than conventional coal.

If we can't eliminate, and we have minimised as much as we can, it may still be necessary to ***render harmless*** those emissions that we can't avoid. This means installing some type of pollution control equipment to reduce emissions to a safe level.

2.2 The main sources, types, controls and impacts of air pollution

There is a wide range of control equipment available to clean exhaust and dirty air before it is released to the atmosphere:

Objective	Treatment
Removal of grit, larger particulates and water droplets	**Gravity separators** The contaminated air is passed into a large chamber where the airflow speed is reduced, allowing particles and droplets to fall into a hopper under the force of gravity. **Cyclones** The contaminated air is passed into a cylindrical chamber that spins the airflow in a spiral. Larger particles are thrown outwards and fall down the walls of the chamber into a hopper.
Removal of small particulates	**Fabric or bag filters** The exhaust passes through a porous fabric filter, usually in the form of a bag, which traps small particles. There is a mechanism for periodically emptying dust that has collected in the bag. Traditional vacuum cleaners work on this principle.
Removal of fine particulates and water droplets	**Electrostatic precipitators** This equipment is often used as the final stage of control on larger facilities such as cement works. The exhaust is first passed over an electrode from which particles receive an electrical charge. The charged particles are then collected on metal plates that are oppositely charged and removed mechanically.
Removal of particulates and gases	**Wet scrubber** The exhaust stream is passed through a spray chamber. The particles and gases are captured by water droplets and removed as sludge.
Removal of vapours and gases	**Adsorption** The exhaust stream is passed over an adsorbent material such as activated charcoal or silica gel.

How does your organisation eliminate or minimise any air pollutants associated with its activities?

Write down your ideas.

EFFECTS OF AIR POLLUTION

The Earth's atmosphere is a global system. Contaminants released into the atmosphere may cause local pollution but also have the potential to contribute to regional and global problems.

Local effects

Public health concerns were one of the first indicators that air pollution had become an issue. By the 19th century, coal smoke from domestic fires and industry had made living in large cities unpleasant and greatly increased the death rate from diseases such as bronchitis.

Particularly poor air quality in London in 1952 is estimated to have:

- **contributed to the early death of around 4,000 people; and**
- **resulted in over 20,000 illnesses[3].**

Local air quality issues affecting human health are still prominent. The growth of 'mega-cities' in developing countries has highlighted the problem of poor urban air quality. The air quality guidelines of the World Health Organisation (WHO) are regularly breached in many cities[4].

Vehicle exhaust emissions contribute greatly to urban air pollution and play a major role in the formation of photochemical smog. These are created when vehicle emissions containing nitrogen oxides and volatile organic compounds (e.g. solvents from paints and fuel vapour) interact in the presence of sunlight to produce harmful secondary pollutants, including ground-level ozone. The young and elderly are particularly susceptible to the effects of poor local air quality. Health problems include shortness of breath, coughing, bronchitis, pneumonia, heart stress or failure, and premature ageing of lung tissue.

Local air quality issues are not restricted to human beings. Ground-level ozone can also cause damage to vegetation, affecting agricultural crops and wildlife.

Regional effects

The long-range transport of air pollution from cities and centres of industry can also have national and regional impacts.

Oxides of nitrogen (NOx) and sulphur (SOx) can travel up to 1,000 kilometres from their emission source and react with moisture in the atmosphere to create 'acid rain'. This affects trees by damaging their leaves and bark, making them more vulnerable to disease, weather and insects. Toxic amounts of aluminium and iron may also be released from soils, further damaging trees and other plants. Lake eco-systems that receive acid rain may become acidic themselves and this can kill fish eggs. At higher levels of acidity, aluminium may build up in the water and kill adult fish, on which other animals such as birds feed.

It is thought that around 20,000 lakes in Scandinavia have been affected by acid rain, with 4,000 being so acidic that no life can survive in them.

Acid rain also attacks many stone buildings leading to structural damage and spoiling decorative features such as sculptures and monuments.

Dust and particulate matter can also be transported over many hundreds of kilometres.

The indiscriminate burning of rainforests in Indonesia has created episodes of severe air pollution in Singapore, where smoke and debris from the fires caused a thick haze over the city lasting many weeks during 2013.

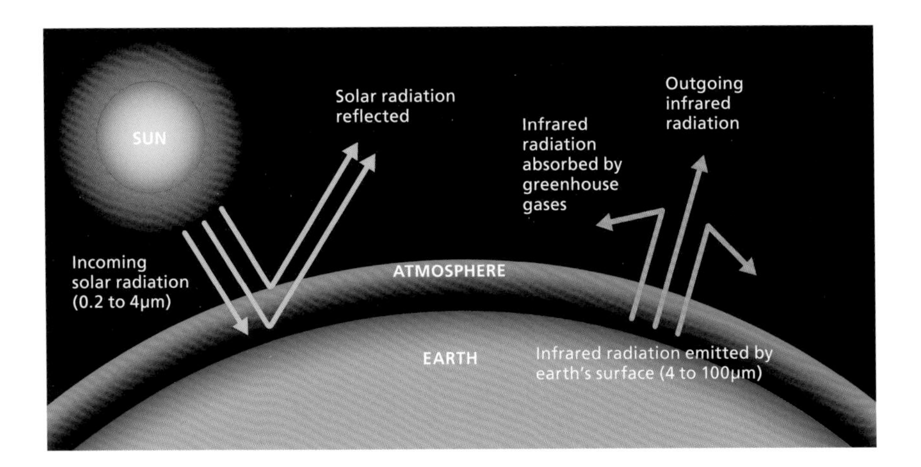

Global effects

The global effects of air pollution – ***climate change*** and ***ozone depletion*** - have now moved to the top of the international agenda.

Climate change

We have seen how burning fossil fuels inevitably results in the emission of carbon dioxide. Levels of this gas measured in the atmosphere have risen by more than 25% over the last 150 years, due to the greatly increased use of fossil fuels since the Industrial Revolution began[5].

Over this period there has been an increase in the average temperature of the atmosphere of almost 1°C. There is now little doubt that ***global warming*** and rising carbon dioxide levels are linked through a phenomenon called the ***greenhouse effect***.

The Earth is warmed by energy from the Sun and directs some of this energy back towards space as infra-red radiation. Some of this radiation is absorbed by ***greenhouse gases*** that occur naturally in the atmosphere (notably water vapour, carbon dioxide and methane) - the effect of this is to warm the Earth's surface and the lower atmosphere. Man-made emissions of greenhouse gases, especially carbon dioxide, are now believed to be artificially enhancing the greenhouse effect, leading to global warming.

Global warming is quite likely to trigger changes in the Earth's climate, with potentially very serious consequences.

Food-producing areas might begin to suffer droughts.

There are also likely to be more extreme and disruptive weather events such as storms and floods.

Ozone depletion

Ozone is a gas which causes pollution when it occurs at ground level. Most of the ozone in the Earth's atmosphere is high up in a layer called the stratosphere, at an altitude of 15 to 50 kilometres. This ***ozone layer*** actually protects life on Earth by absorbing some of the damaging ultraviolet (UV) radiation from the Sun. In the 1980s it was observed that ozone was starting to disappear in parts of the stratosphere, with the risk of enhanced levels of UV radiation reaching the Earth's surface. UV radiation causes sunburn in humans. Prolonged exposure to higher levels of UV radiation is likely to result in a much higher incidence of skin cancers and eye disorders. UV light can also be damaging to plants and crops.

Ozone depletion is caused by emissions of a group of man-made chemicals containing chlorine and bromine, principally:

- chlorofluorocarbons (CFCs) used in fridges and aerosol sprays;
- halons used in fire protection systems;
- carbon tetrachloride used in fire extinguishers and as a dry-cleaning solvent; and
- methyl chloroform used as a cleaning solvent.

The ***Montreal Protocol on Substances that Deplete the Ozone Layer*** (1987)[6] is an international agreement to phase-out the production and use of a wide range of ozone-depleting chemicals such as those mentioned previously.

Practice Question

PRACTICE QUESTION

Q2 The main source of air pollution in the world is

A waste incineration.

B air travel.

C destroying tropical forests.

D burning fossil fuels.

2.3 The main sources, controls and impacts of water pollution

Water is essential for life:

- We need clean, fresh water to drink and for washing.
- Our food crops need water for irrigation.
- Rivers, lakes and the seas provide habitats for wildlife and provide us with food and places of recreation.

This highlights the need to conserve water by using water resources wisely, and not polluting the water that is available to us.

SOURCES OF WATER POLLUTION

Domestic waste waters

In 1858 the smell from the River Thames in London was so bad, because of untreated human waste, that Parliament and the law courts considered abandoning the city. This episode was known as "The Big Stink". Similar problems occurred in many major cities across the industrial world as populations expanded rapidly and untreated human waste was discharged into local rivers.

Domestic waste is still the greatest potential source of water pollution throughout the world. This waste is often referred to as ***sewage***, because it is usually disposed of via a network of underground pipes called sewers.

Most of the fresh water that we use ends up being discharged down drains and into the sewer system. This includes everything that we flush away down toilets, and water from sinks, bathrooms, dishwashers and washing machines. Sewage comes not only from our homes but also from commercial premises such as offices, restaurants, hotels and industry.

Rainwater that runs off roofs, pavements and roads may also drain into the sewer system, especially in older parts of towns and cities.

The volume of sewage that needs to be disposed of is enormous: every single day, the UK has to dispose of 11 billion litres of sewage[7]. A significant proportion used to be discharged directly into rivers, estuaries and the sea, with little or no treatment. Nowadays, almost all UK sewage is treated to international standards, before the final effluent is discharged into receiving waters.

Domestic waste water from many of the world's cities – especially in the developing world – is discharged untreated and this represents a major source of water pollution.

The main pollutants in sewage are:

Pollutant	Potential impacts
Solid debris such as plastic waste, wood and textiles	Causes unsightly litter on the surface of waterways and around river banks.
Organic material – human waste and food residues	Uses up oxygen as it decays. May strip so much oxygen from the receiving water that fish and other wildlife cannot survive.
Suspended solids - silt, sand and organic particles suspended in the water	May smother plants and animals that live on the bottom of the receiving water. Clouds the water, reducing the light available for plants to grow. Many toxic contaminants adhere to these particles, which may be eaten by aquatic animals. Disease-causing viruses and bacteria often adhere to particulates.
Nutrients - nitrogen and phosphorus compounds	Cause excessive growth of microscopic plants, which strip oxygen from the water.
Toxics - metals such as copper, nickel and lead, and oil	In sufficient doses can poison wildlife and humans.

2.3 The main sources, controls and impacts of water pollution

Industrial discharges

Many industries generate liquid effluents as by-products of the processes they operate.

- Sites may discharge these effluents into the sewer system, where they become mixed with domestic waste water and pass through sewage treatment works.
- Many larger industrial sites make discharges directly into local waters.

Companies that discharge effluents directly into local waters are likely to operate their own treatment plants, to ensure that legal standards are met. In many parts of the world, however, legal controls may be weak or poorly enforced.

The following industries are likely to generate significant volumes of liquid effluents from their operating processes:

Industry	Water pollution issues
Textiles	Washing, dyeing and rinsing fibres generates large volumes of waste water contaminated with a range of chemicals. These include residues of pesticides that have been used on raw materials such as cotton crops and wool, etc.
Mining	Water that is drained from mine workings is likely to contain high levels of toxic metals.
Manufacture and bottling of soft drinks and alcoholic beverages	Washing down equipment and bottles and disposing of waste product generates large volumes of waste water.
Pulp and paper manufacture	Pulping timber to make paper uses very high volumes of water and results in an effluent with high levels of suspended solids. Highly toxic residues of chlorine from paper bleaching may also be present.
PVC production (chloralkali processes)	Traditional chloralkali processes involve the use of mercury electrodes. Effluents may contain highly toxic mercury compounds.
Titanium dioxide production	This common white pigment is extracted from natural minerals in a process that generates high volumes of acidic liquid sludge.
Milk processing	Washing down equipment and bottles and disposing of waste product generates large volumes of waste water.

Some industries also use water for cooling their plant and equipment. Coolant water that is discharged back into the environment may be largely free from contaminants but will have gained heat. Discharging hot coolant can raise the temperature of a river by over 10°C. The warmer the water, the less oxygen it is able to hold in solution and fish in particular suffer because of this. Industrial sectors that often use large volumes of water for cooling are:

- electricity generation;
- oil refining;
- steel making; and
- cement manufacture.

Unplanned discharges

The sources of water pollution that we have discussed so far all result from planned activities. Unplanned discharges must also be taken into account when considering sources of water pollution.

Accidental spills and leaks of fuel and liquid chemicals are the most common cause of unplanned discharges. Spills often happen when tanks are being re-filled, or decanted. Old or disused tanks may also leak if they become damaged or corroded.

What do you think is the likely outcome of a spillage of hazardous liquid such as diesel oil?

Remember the model that we used to identify environmental impacts: ***source – pathway – receptor***. If there is a spill then we certainly have a source of contaminant. Is there a pathway by which the contaminant can reach a sensitive receptor?

If a spill of oil occurs near an open drain, it might get into the drainage system (the pathway) and eventually reach a local river (the receptor).

Spills that happen on unmade ground may contaminate the surrounding land and pass into the groundwater.

2.3 The main sources, controls and impacts of water pollution

Do you think there is any risk of spills of hazardous liquids at your place of work?

What liquids might be involved?

Agriculture

Potential sources of water pollution are often associated with agricultural operations such as:

- storage of fuel for machinery;
- other hazardous liquids, e.g. pesticides;
- large volumes of animal waste stored in slurry pits;
- effluent from feed stores, especially silage; and
- storage and uploading of large volumes of milk.

Agricultural pollution incidents usually involve unplanned releases of contaminants which find their way into local rivers, through spillages or failure of the storage systems.

We may think of milk as being a very benign product, but if a large spill were to get into a local river, it would rapidly strip the oxygen from the water as it was broken down by micro-organisms.

The most significant form of water pollution associated with agriculture occurs due to the run-off of fertilisers and pesticides from fields.

It is common practice to apply artificial nitrate-based and phosphate-based fertilisers on fields of crops, especially cereals. If fertilisers are applied at the wrong time of year, or under adverse weather conditions, a significant amount – especially nitrates – can leach off the land and get into drainage systems and from there into rivers. This type of pollution is known as ***diffuse source***, because the contaminant does not enter the river via a distinct ***point source***, such as a single discharge pipe.

High levels of nitrates:

- Cause excessive growth of microscopic plants in the river; these plants remove oxygen from the water so that fish and other wildlife cannot survive.
- May be dangerous where rivers are used for drinking water supplies. Water purification processes do not always remove soluble nitrates and public water supplies may therefore have raised concentrations of nitrate. This is no problem for adults, but babies metabolise nitrates differently, producing substances in their blood that are potentially lethal.

CONTROL OF WATER POLLUTION

We have already seen that there is a general hierarchy of approaches for controlling pollution: ***eliminate – minimise – render harmless***.

If we ***eliminate*** the source of a contaminant, then clearly it can't cause pollution.

Chlorine has traditionally been used to bleach wood pulp when making white paper. This process results in a liquid effluent that contains toxic and very long-lasting organochlorine compounds. The paper industry has responded to concerns about pollution from these discharges by devising new processes for paper bleaching that are completely free of chlorine.

Polyvinyl Chloride (PVC) is one of the most widely used plastics in the world, e.g. for making window and door frames, electric cabling, piping and flooring. The traditional method of producing PVC involves an electrochemical process that uses mercury electrodes. Discharges from this process have resulted in this highly toxic metal building up over many years in rivers and estuaries, such as the River Mersey in England. Advances in technology have now eliminated the need to use mercury electrodes so there are no more mercury discharges.

It is impossible to eliminate all sources of waste water, e.g. sewage, but the amount of domestic sewage we produce does depend on the amount of water we use. So if we ***minimise*** our water consumption, we will reduce the amount of waste water that needs to be disposed of.

How could you minimise your water consumption at home?

You could:

- take a shower instead of a bath;
- wash the car less often;
- install a toilet that uses less water for flushing;
- fix a dripping tap.

Minimising water consumption is also the key to reducing discharges from many industrial processes. Companies like Coca Cola use water to make their product, but also create a lot of waste water from washing down equipment and washing and rinsing bottles. Most major drinks companies have now set themselves targets to save water and this has the added effect of reducing their discharges of contaminated water[8].

2.3 The main sources, controls and impacts of water pollution

Think of the opportunities that your organisation might have to save water.

Try to write down at least three ideas.

Discharges that we can't eliminate, or minimise, need to be ***rendered harmless***. We have seen that accidental spills and leaks of harmful liquids, e.g. fuel stored in tanks, are particularly significant sources of water pollution. What practical things can we do to prevent spills? The answers are mostly straightforward:

- Make sure that tanks and other containers are sited safely. This usually means placing them within some sort of secondary containment, e.g. on an impervious concrete base surrounded by a protective wall (bund) and well away from any drains.
- Inspect the condition of the tanks and containers regularly to make sure they are not damaged or corroded. Repairs and maintenance must be done without delay.
- Label tanks and containers so that what they contain is clear.
- Have procedures to ensure that transfers of liquids to or from containers are done carefully and safely.

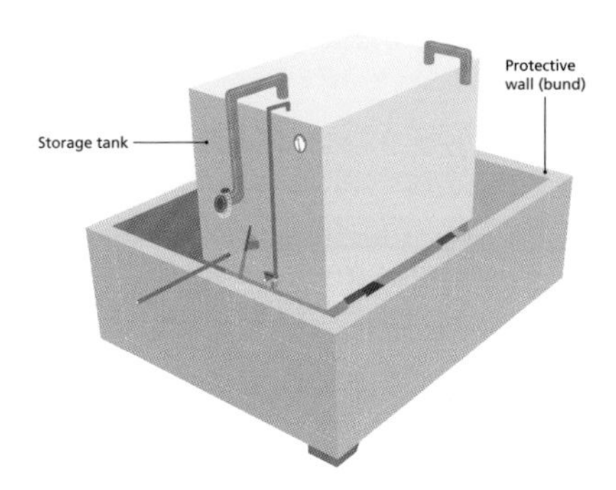

If, despite our best efforts, a spill should occur, we need to have a plan in place to prevent the spillage from getting into drains and watercourses, or from soaking into the ground and contaminating groundwater. Many organisations have spill kits, located in high-risk areas, which contain absorbent materials in the form of granules and cushions or socks to prevent spills from moving far from the point of origin.

Planned discharges to the aquatic environment need to be treated so that the level of contaminants is below that at which significant environmental damage will be caused. These limits are often specified in legal discharge consents or permits.

Treatment of effluents most often involves the removal of particulate material from the liquid. The main techniques for achieving this are the following:

Objective	Treatment
Removal of large solids (wood, plastics, textiles)	**Screening** Usually a simple steel mesh that filters out debris.
Removal of grit and larger particles	**Sedimentation** The effluent is transferred into a large tank, where the water flow is very slow or stationary. This allows particles to sink to the bottom by gravity. **Flotation** Air is bubbled up through the liquid and particles are trapped by the air bubbles. This creates a scum on the surface that can be removed mechanically.
Removal of fine particulates	**Filtration** The effluent is passed into a tank that contains a layer of filter medium – such as sand – in the bottom. The effluent passes by gravity through the filter to a drain in the bottom of the tank.
Removal of very fine particles	**Coagulation** Some particles are so fine that they will not settle out of suspension by gravity. The effluent is treated by adding special chemicals (coagulants) that cause the fine particles to stick together into larger clumps that can be removed by filtration or sedimentation.
Removal of organic particles	**Biological treatment** The effluent is passed into an aerated tank that contains a population of micro-organisms that feed on the organic material. In some systems, the micro-organisms develop as a film on the surface of a gravel bed. The effluent is trickled over the gravel bed by a system of rotating feed pipes.

Introduction Element 1.1 Element 1.2 Element 1.3 Element 2.1 Element 2.2 Element 2.3 Element 2.4 Element 2.5 Element 2.6 Element 2.7

Chemical treatment of an effluent may also be necessary, e.g. the pH (alkalinity or acidity) may need to be adjusted by dosing with lime (calcium oxide/ hydroxide) or an acid (hydrochloric acid).

EFFECTS OF WATER POLLUTION

Before we consider the effects of water pollution, we need to think about how water is distributed over the planet:

- Oceans, seas and estuaries contain around 97% of all the water on the planet.
- Most of the freshwater is bound up in the polar ice caps and glaciers (around 2%).
- The remaining freshwater that is available for us to use (just 1% of the Earth's total water) is distributed between rivers, lakes and underground aquifers (groundwater).

Human life depends on having clean freshwater to drink and for irrigating crops. This emphasises the need to minimise pollution of our limited reserves of freshwater (rivers, lakes, groundwater).

Human health

Water pollution has probably caused more human deaths than wars. We have seen how uncontrolled dumping of human waste in the River Thames in London in the 19th century created an unbearable smell. This waste also contaminated drinking water sources in the city with the bacteria that cause cholera. Around 10,000 people died of this disease as a result.

There have been several pandemics of cholera across the globe in the last 150 years, resulting in huge loss of life. It has been estimated that around 800,000 people died of cholera in India alone in the first 20 years of the 20th century. In 2010, cholera was estimated to be still causing over 100,000 deaths every year around the world.

Litter and debris at the side of a river or on a beach is unpleasant. It spoils recreational enjoyment of wild places when they have been damaged by pollution.

Habitats and eco-systems

Many major rivers in industrialised countries became almost devoid of fish during the 19th century and are only now recovering as tougher controls on pollution have started to take effect.

Fish, birds and other aquatic wildlife depend on clean water as much as humans.

Water pollution in rivers, lakes, estuaries and the oceans can affect fish and other aquatic animals, and aquatic plants as well as destroying habitats and eco-systems. Additionally, the pollution can also have an effect on habitats and eco-systems in the surrounding environment such as riverbanks and shorelines.

Some of the main effects of water pollution include:

- **Build-up of toxins:** Heavy metals and pesticides may be acutely toxic to some wild animals and plants. Some of these pollutants are long-lasting and can be concentrated up the food chain, so that larger predators, such as otters and dolphins, are exposed to greater concentrations. For example, a factory in the Japanese coastal town of Minamata discharged small quantities of the highly toxic substance, methyl mercury, into the local bay. This was ingested by shellfish and concentrated in their flesh. Around 1,500 local people who ate shellfish subsequently died from mercury poisoning.
- **Oxygen depletion:** Aquatic animals and plants need oxygen to live, just as we do. Many organic wastes (e.g. those found in sewage or farm-animal slurry) can dramatically reduce the concentration of oxygen in river water. The micro-organisms which break down the pollution use up the oxygen in the surrounding water.
- **Eutrophication:** This also results in oxygen being stripped from the water. It can be caused by nutrients from agricultural fertilisers which run off the land. These nutrients provide ample food sources for microscopic algae which will then rapidly grow and will consume large amounts of oxygen during the growth process.

The main sources, controls and impacts of water pollution

- **Sediments:** Suspended particles in the water can reduce the amount of sunlight available for algae and other plants to grow. This may have the added effect of harming animals that feed on the plants. In extreme cases, discharges with a high sediment load can physically smother plants and animals living on the bottom of the receiving water. Once the sediment settles this can also alter the flow of water which could result in damage to habitats and eco-systems.
- **Oil:** Oil spills, or deliberate discharges from ships into the sea, often cause the death of seabirds and other animals through suffocation and contamination.
- **Physical and chemical changes:** Some effluents may affect the physical and chemical characteristics of the water body they are discharged into. Discharges of heated coolant water may raise the temperature by several degrees. This may kill some animals and plants that are not adapted to high temperatures and will reduce the amount of oxygen dissolved in the water.
  Some discharges may affect the pH of water, e.g. making it more acidic, which many aquatic animals cannot tolerate.

Practice Question

PRACTICE QUESTION

Q3 Which is an example of a diffuse source of water pollution?

- A The discharge from a sewage treatment works.
- B An oil spill getting into a site drainage system.
- C High water consumption.
- D Run-off from the application of nitrate fertiliser to a cereal crop getting into the local river.

2.4 The main sources, controls and impacts of environmental noise

Damage to people's hearing through exposure to high levels of noise in the workplace, e.g. from engines and other machinery, is a well-recognised occupational health issue.

A different, but related, problem is disturbance from ***environmental noise***. What do we mean by this?

Most people have experienced disturbance and irritation from unwanted noise that interferes with life at home or perhaps has prevented a good night's sleep in a hotel room. Noise from a wide variety of sources can travel considerable distances and affect the tranquillity and enjoyment of life. This is sometimes also referred to as ***noise nuisance***.

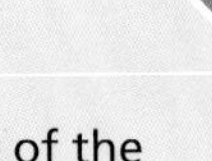

Think about occasions when you have been disturbed by noise.

Write down the sources of the noise that troubled you.

SOURCES OF ENVIRONMENTAL NOISE

Residential neighbours

Environmental noise is most likely to disturb us in our own homes. It often comes from the activities of other residents in the neighbourhood. Sources of noise that may cause annoyance include:

- loud music from radios and other sound systems;
- use of equipment such as power drills and grass cutters; and
- dogs barking persistently or late at night.

Commercial premises

Nightclubs and commercial premises such as warehouses that are situated in residential areas may also be a source of environmental noise. This may come from:

- music entertainment;
- public address systems;
- rowdy customers entering and leaving premises;
- delivery vans and lorries coming and going; and
- intruder alarms left unattended.

Transport

Major roads and airports can have a major impact on the lives of people who live nearby:

- Engine noise from motorways can travel hundreds of metres – at night we can often hear traffic noise from roads that are several miles away.
- Large jet aircraft engines are intensely noisy, especially during take-off and landing. Many established airports are quite close to major centres of population.

Construction sites

Construction work often takes place near town centres and in residential areas. It typically involves activities that are potentially noisy, including:

- the use of heavy equipment such as excavators and cranes;
- pile driving, especially at larger sites;
- the use of powered hand-tools; and
- lorries and vans delivering materials and taking away debris.

The main sources, controls and impacts of environmental noise

Heavy industry

The activities of traditional heavy industries are often significantly noisy, including the use of:

- heavy presses and hammers to form and shape metal parts in forges, shipyards and vehicle assembly plants;
- turbines in electricity generation plants;
- explosives and rock-crushing equipment used for mining and quarrying activities; and
- general machinery such as conveyor systems and air compressors.

Agriculture

Modern agriculture is highly mechanised and noise can be more noticeable in the countryside. Noise from agricultural activities is often associated with the use of:

- Mobile machinery, e.g. tractors and harvesters, with harvesting sometimes being undertaken around the clock.
- Bird-scarers that simulate loud gunshots.

Does your organisation create noise in the environment?

Has your organisation ever had any complaints about noise?

CONTROL OF ENVIRONMENTAL NOISE

Opportunities for controlling environmental noise fall into three broad categories:

1. Stop, or reduce, the source of the noise

If an activity such as playing a radio is causing a nuisance, the most effective way of controlling the nuisance is to turn off the radio.

In many circumstances it simply isn't possible to stop the source of the noise. There may though be opportunities to reduce the intensity of the noise source, e.g. by:

- replacing noisy equipment with a quieter alternative; or
- placing the equipment in a sound-proof enclosure.

2. Limit the transmission of the noise

It may be possible to engineer a physical barrier, positioned between the source of the noise and the receiver, to limit the amount of noise transmitted.

3. Protect the receiver from the noise

It may be possible to protect the receiver by installing some kind of noise insulation, such as double-glazing.

In practice, the control of any noise problem is likely to involve a combination of management and engineering controls, depending on the particular circumstances.

Management controls

Management controls tend to be more cost-effective than engineering approaches, because they are usually aimed at stopping, or reducing, the source of noise and rarely involve much expenditure. Typical management controls include:

- **Hours of working:** Restricting working to normal hours of business, e.g. not allowing deliveries to be made at night or at weekends, when local residents are likely to be resting. Places of entertainment such as nightclubs are often required to close by a certain time in the evening.
- **Sound equipment:** The use of public address systems and radios in commercial premises can be restricted and volume limits set.
- **Vehicle routes:** Regular lorry routes that pass through residential areas can be changed to avoid passing through the most built-up areas. Drivers can be trained to avoid over-use of noisy systems such as air brakes and air-assisted gear changes.

Engineering controls

Engineering controls may involve capital expenditure and take longer to implement than management controls. The following are typical examples of the range of engineering solutions:

- **Isolation:** Very noisy pieces of equipment, such as electricity generating turbines, can be enclosed in insulated, sound-proofed enclosures.
- **Silencers:** Noisy exhausts from engines can be fitted with silencers, as on a car.
- **Damping:** Some heavy pieces of fixed equipment in industrial premises create vibrations that can be transmitted significant distances by the walls and floors of buildings. Mounting such equipment on rubber mountings, or other damping systems, can significantly reduce the transmission of vibrations.

- **Maintenance:** Regular servicing and maintenance can prevent engines and other machines from developing faults – often quite minor – that create excessive noise.
- **Absorption and insulation:** Barriers such as high walls or fences, if carefully situated between the source of noise and the receiver, are often effective in reducing the intensity of the noise for the receiver. Insulating the receptor, e.g. fitting double-glazing to residential properties close to airports, is also a useful way of preventing noise nuisance.

IMPACTS OF ENVIRONMENTAL NOISE

People have a right to the use and enjoyment of their own property, yet noise pollution can be a serious issue.

The perception of noise can be quite subjective. A particular noise may be acceptable to one person, but for someone else it might:

- be intrusive and annoying;
- lead to severe lack of sleep;
- in extreme cases, cause anxiety, stress and depression.

Factors that can affect the perception of noise include:

- **Loudness:** The louder the noise, the more intrusive it is likely to be.
- **Pitch:** Low-pitched sounds, such as vibration from machinery or the bass from sound systems, can be more noticeable.
- **Frequency:** Noise that happens regularly may be anticipated by people who are affected, leading to a greater sense of anxiety.
- **Background levels:** A given sound will travel further and be more noticeable in a quiet rural area than in a busy city street.

Environmental noise may also affect wildlife. Many wild animals – especially birds – use complex calls to communicate with other members of the same species, especially during breeding. Man-made noise can interfere with these communication systems. This is one reason why some animals are not found close to large population centres and major roads.

Practice Question

PRACTICE QUESTION

Q4 The most effective way to reduce environmental noise is to

A install double-glazing.

B stop the source of the noise.

C use ear defenders.

D limit hours of working.

2.5 Types of waste

Waste, in a general sense, is any unwanted material. We all need to dispose of unwanted materials, whether from our homes or at work, and we are said to live in a 'throw-away' society. Every person in the European Union, for example, generates around 500 kg of waste every year[9].

What do you routinely dispose of at home?

Write down these items and materials.

In the European Union, the legal definition of waste is:

"any substance or object which the holder discards or intends or is required to discard".

This description is clearly very wide! If you look at the list you made of the things you typically throw away at home, this probably includes a wide range of items, made up of all sorts of different types of material - potato peelings, old newspapers, empty food tins, broken electrical appliances, etc.

If we think about wastes that are created by commercial and industrial activities, the list gets longer. In fact, any item or material that we consume in human society can eventually end up as waste.

Disposing of our waste mountain is one of the biggest environmental challenges facing society. If we are going to devise the safest and most cost-effective approaches to waste management (see section 2.6), it's helpful to know exactly what we are dealing with, because different wastes need to be treated in different ways.

One way of classifying wastes is by the activity that generated them. Policy-makers and legislators often refer to the following waste categories:

- **Household** - domestic waste from people's homes.
- **Commercial** - waste from shops and offices.
- **Municipal** - waste that is disposed of by municipal authorities and is usually a mixture of household and commercial waste.
- **Construction** - waste from the construction industry.
- **Industrial** - sometimes further classified by industry, e.g. mining, petroleum, iron and steel.
- **Agricultural** - waste from farms.
- **Food** - waste from food processing plants, canteens and restaurants.

It is more useful, however, to classify a waste by its physical, chemical and biological properties because these properties determine how any waste, regardless of its source, can be effectively and safely dealt with.

Legislation governing waste disposal around the world varies but is becoming increasingly harmonised. The following major categories of waste are almost universally recognised:

- **Inert:** As the name suggests, this is waste that is stable. This means that it will not degrade physically, or react chemically, or be decomposed by the action of micro-organisms. Construction wastes such as brick, concrete and glass are usually considered to be inert, providing they have not been contaminated with other materials.
- **Hazardous:** These are wastes that pose a particular danger to human health and/or to the environment. Many specific definitions of hazardous waste are used around the world, but waste is usually classified as hazardous if it has at least one of the following properties[10]:

Hazardous waste properties	Examples
Explosive or highly flammable	Fireworks; distress flares; ammunition; liquid fuels such as petrol, diesel, fuel oil; solvents such as white spirit or paint stripper.
Highly reactive and/or corrosive	Strong acids and alkalis, e.g. battery acid or bleach.
Toxic to humans	Pesticides; wood preservatives; medicines.
Biologically hazardous	Materials that have the potential to be infectious or carcinogenic, e.g. contaminated textiles such as bandages; asbestos.
Toxic to the environment	Oil; batteries containing lead, cadmium or mercury; fluorescent lighting tubes.

2.5 Types of waste

Two categories of hazardous waste - ***clinical*** and ***radioactive*** - are often treated separately in legislation, because they require special methods of treatment and disposal.

Type of hazardous waste	Examples
Clinical	Waste from healthcare activities, such as: • human tissue, including blood samples • faeces and urine • swabs and dressings • syringe needles and scalpels • pharmaceutical products
Radioactive	This covers: • high volume wastes from the nuclear power industry • smaller volumes of waste produced from the use of radioactive substances in laboratories and measuring and monitoring equipment

- **Non-hazardous:** By definition, this covers any waste that does not have any of the properties of hazardous waste. It includes most things that you dispose of at home.
  This does not mean that 'non-hazardous' waste has no impact on the environment. If, for example, waste that is biodegradable (potato peelings, old newspapers) is disposed of in a landfill site, it may be broken down by the action of micro-organisms and generate methane gas which is a potent greenhouse gas.

Write down the discarded items and other materials that your organisation routinely disposes of as waste.

Group these under the following waste categories:

- **inert;**
- **hazardous; and**
- **non-hazardous.**

Practice Question

PRACTICE QUESTION

Q5 Which is an example of an inert waste?

- A Clean bricks from a demolition site.
- B Grass cuttings.
- C Glass bottles that have been used to hold chemicals.
- D Cardboard.

2.6 Waste management

The management of waste is one of the biggest challenges facing industrialised societies. The World Bank estimates that the amount of municipal solid waste that needs to be disposed of from the world's cities will rise to around 2.2 billion tonnes per year by 2025[11]. Most of this waste is either dumped in holes in the ground (landfilled) or incinerated and this is a major source of air, water and land pollution.

Creating and disposing of waste also represents a huge loss of resources – think of all the materials and energy that have gone into producing the items that you throw away at home.

For businesses, waste creation can also have high costs, as they must:

- pay for raw materials, some of which may go to waste; and
- pay for waste to be collected and disposed of.

This means that good waste management is usually accompanied by significant cost savings.

THE WASTE HIERARCHY

National and international strategies for waste management are driven by the need to:

- conserve resources; and
- minimise pollution.

The approach is based on the ***waste hierarchy*** - this makes waste prevention the most preferred option and disposal the least desirable.

BEST OPTION

PREVENT

- Making products more efficiently.
- Making products last longer, e.g. by making them more durable

REDUCE

- Designing products that use less materials.
- Using the correct amount of any product for the purpose intended, so there is no waste surplus.
- Designing products so that they can be easily re-used.

RE-USE

- Refurbishing and repairing old products or equipment so that they can be used by someone else.

RECOVER

- Recycling discarded items to recover materials that can be used to make new products.
- Recycling discarded items to recover energy, e.g. by using recovered materials as fuel.

DISPOSAL

- Landfill and incineration with no energy recovery.

WORST OPTION

Prevent

We avoid all the problems associated with waste disposal if we don't create waste at all.

Don't waste raw materials during manufacture. Good quality control will ensure that fewer rejects are produced.

Don't throw away your mobile phone every time a new model comes out.

Reduce

The less of any material or product we use, the less potential there is for waste to be created.

Make the same product, but with less materials, e.g. food tins and drinks bottles are now much thinner and lighter than they used to be.

When carrying out any task, such as painting a building, calculate the correct amount of material (paint) needed to complete the job. This avoids buying surplus material, which needs to be disposed of when the job is finished.

Re-use

Products are often discarded when they are still functional, because:

- they are no longer needed; or
- a product with a higher specification is required; or
- fashions have changed.

These products often have a real value to other people or organisations.

Many companies now donate their redundant IT equipment such as PCs and laptops to educational establishments and charities.

An enormous range of goods, such as clothes, pictures, furniture, cooking utensils and books, are donated to charity shops. This is a major source of income for many charities, as well as a cheap source of goods for many people. Another growth area for passing on unwanted items for re-use by others is the use of on-line auction sites.

Soft drinks used to be delivered in glass bottles that were sent back to the bottler to be cleaned and re-filled.

Do you think we will see a revival in this practice?

Recovery

Discarded items that are recycled can be processed to recover materials that can then be used to make something new. The easiest products to recycle are those that are made of only a single material, e.g. glass bottles, but a wide range of products can be recycled. In urban areas around the world, schemes are now being introduced to collect products separately for recycling and recovery, including:

- glass bottles;
- aluminium and steel cans;
- plastic bottles;
- old newspapers and magazines;
- cardboard packaging; and
- plastic shrink-wrap.

Over 80% of the newsprint used by The Guardian, one of the UK's leading national newspapers, is made from recycled paper[12].

Waste organic materials, e.g. food and grass cuttings, may also be collected to produce compost used in gardens and landscaping schemes.

Every country in the EU has been set the target of recovering 50% of domestic and commercial waste by 2020[13].

Recycled waste can also be processed to recover energy.

The heat from incinerating waste paper and card can be used to create steam, which is then used to generate electricity or for heating buildings.

Methane gas is generated from the decay of organic wastes in landfill sites. This can be collected and used to generate electricity.

Write down the items you separate in your own home for recycling collections.

Disposal
Responsible disposal of waste should be the last resort.

There will always be some waste for which there is no alternative except disposal, because:

- none of the preferred options in the hierarchy are possible;
- recycling operations generate residues of material that cannot be used.

The two main methods of final disposal are:

- landfill; and
- incineration (with no energy recovery).

List the types of waste material that your organisation currently sends for disposal.

Are there opportunities for moving any of these materials up the waste hierarchy?

MANAGING WASTE

Managing waste in accordance with the waste hierarchy presents both challenges and opportunities for any organisation. The following are practical steps that an organisation should take to manage waste responsibly.

How barriers to re-use and recycling can be overcome

If waste cannot be prevented, re-use and recycling are usually the best practicable options. Obstacles in the way of improving re-use and recycling rates include:

- **The economics of re-use:** Unfortunately, it is often cheaper for manufacturers to create new containers for drinks and similar products, than to organise the collection, washing and re-use of old containers returned by customers. There may also be safety concerns about re-using discarded items for food purposes.
- **Culture and attitudes:** Separating items that can be re-used or recycled involves a little thought and effort. Some individuals, at home or in the workplace, may not be prepared to do this.

- **Markets for recycled materials:** A great driver for recycling is the money that organisations can get for their separated wastes such as cardboard, glass and plastic. Unfortunately, the price that the market will pay for recycled materials has been very volatile. Sometimes it is so low that there is little financial incentive to recycle.
- **Storage:** Separating different kinds of waste for recycling requires more containers and more space. This can be a real problem in some cramped homes and workplaces.

These barriers are gradually being overcome as re-use and recycling practices become more accepted in society. Public facilities for collecting recyclables, including household collections, have improved. Markets for recycled materials are becoming more reliable, as the range of products that can be made from recycled materials continues to expand.

Most organisations find that re-use and recycling rates can be improved through positive promotion, such as campaigns where:

- there is strong support from senior management;
- resources have been employed to provide good facilities for segregating waste;
- workers are educated in the benefits and encouraged, e.g. by setting targets and holding competitions; and
- cost savings are widely publicised.

The implementation of an environmental management system can also encourage and improve waste re-use/recycling rates.

Responsible waste management

Waste materials can create pollution and hazardous wastes may also represent an immediate danger to people. All organisations therefore have a duty to manage the wastes that they produce responsibly.

2.6 Waste management

Every waste producer should take care of the waste that they produce, from the point at which it is generated, until it is safely disposed of. In the European Union, this good practice is underpinned by directives. Key actions are:

- segregate different types of waste at source;
- store waste safely and securely; and
- ensure the safe onward transport (by an approved carrier) of the waste and appropriate final disposal.

Segregation, identification and labelling

All organisations produce different types of waste, which may require quite different treatments. Some wastes may be readily recycled, whereas others may not. Hazardous wastes always require special treatment and there may be particular legal requirements for other categories of waste.

Responsible waste management begins by ensuring that different waste types are identified at source and kept separate. It is particularly important to:

- know which wastes have hazardous properties; and
- keep these away from non-hazardous wastes to avoid cross-contamination.

Certain hazardous wastes may also be incompatible and there may be a danger of fire or poisonous gases being released if they come into contact with each other.

Wastes need to be clearly labelled, so that everyone who comes into contact with them knows exactly what material they are dealing with.

Safe storage

Wastes must not be allowed to escape and cause pollution, or create a threat to people's safety. This means that each waste type should be stored in an appropriate container.

Paper should be held in an enclosed container to prevent it from being blown around.

Liquid wastes should be placed in tanks or containers with secondary protection and be isolated from drainage systems.

In addition, all waste containers should:

- not be stacked on top of each other;
- be regularly inspected for corrosion and other damage;
- be replaced or repaired immediately if damage/corrosion is noted;
- be protected against unauthorised access.

Transportation

Good waste management requires producers to take responsibility for the wastes that they create, until they have been safely treated (e.g. recycled) or disposed of. This means ensuring that anyone who transports, treats or disposes of their waste does so appropriately and in compliance with local laws. It involves:

- Checking that waste collectors and those operating treatment or disposal facilities have the correct environmental permits (permissions).
- Providing documentation with any waste transfer that accurately describes the waste.

Documentation

Good international practice now requires that the transfer of waste between parties (waste producer, carrier(s), processors, etc.) should be documented. The main principles are:

- A transfer note (or consignment note)* must be completed and stay with the waste until the point of final disposal.
- The transfer note should provide details of:
  - the waste producer;
  - who the waste is being transferred to;
  - the exact nature of the waste;
  - the quantity of the waste; and
  - how the waste is contained.

*Terminology for waste disposal documentation may be different in your country.

It is good practice for every party involved in the waste chain (producer, transporter, and disposer) to keep copies of this documentation for a number of years; many countries will have their own legislation with regard to waste disposal.

Packaging waste

A significant proportion of the waste in industrial economies consists of waste packaging.

It has been estimated that around 10% of the waste in the European Union consists of waste packaging, equivalent to a staggering 150 kg for every person each year[14].

To minimise the burden that this places on the waste management infrastructure each EU member state was given the target of recycling 55% of its packaging waste by the end of 2008. They have to continue to meet this minimum target and have the freedom to set even higher targets.

Unilever is one of the largest producers of foods and cleaning products. In 2013, the company made a commitment to reduce the weight of packaging on its products by a third, by 2020[15].

It aims to achieve this by:

- **eliminating unnecessary packaging;**
- **using lightweight materials;**
- **design changes; and**
- **developing concentrated versions of some of its products, e.g. washing powders.**

How much of the waste produced in your household is made up of packaging for food, drink and cleaning products?

Electrical and electronic waste

People now use more and more electrical and electronic devices, including:

- appliances such as fridges, microwave ovens and lighting units;
- laptop computers;
- mobile phones; and
- television sets and sound systems.

There has been a corresponding increase in the amount of electrical and electronic waste and this is the fastest growing waste sector.

Electrical and electronic devices are complex and contain many substances that are toxic and long-lasting in the environment.

Practice Question

Electronic circuitry contains several metals that may leach out of equipment that is discarded in landfill sites. These include lead, cadmium, chromium and mercury, all of which are potentially toxic to people and the environment.

A number of chemicals that are persistent pollutants are also used in the manufacture of electronic equipment. 'Brominated flame retardants' are a cause of particular concern. They are intended to reduce the risk of electronic equipment catching fire and are typically added to:

- printed circuit boards;
- plastic covers; and
- connectors and cables.

The European Union has issued a Directive which seeks to:

- reduce the amount of waste electrical and electronic equipment going to landfill; and
- encourage maximum re-use and recycling.

PRACTICE QUESTION

Q6 Which would be the preferred method for dealing with empty cardboard boxes used to deliver paper to an office?

A Burning.

B Collection by the local authority for landfill disposal.

C Collection by the local authority for recycling.

D Re-using the boxes.

2.7 Dealing with environmental emergencies

In 1986, a major fire at a warehouse in Switzerland released chemicals into the River Rhine, causing a massive number of wildlife deaths for hundreds of miles downstream[16]. Events of this size are rare, but minor emergency incidents, e.g. spillages of fuel, are quite common and a significant source of local pollution.

This section looks more closely at environmental emergencies and how they can be managed.

TYPICAL ENVIRONMENTAL INCIDENTS

The risk of an unplanned incident occurring can be greatly reduced by good planning and management. However, there is always some potential for accidents and, as well as posing a risk to humans, these may also have an environmental impact.

Spillage

Many organisations store hazardous liquids on site. Perhaps the most frequently recorded environmental incidents involve spills of fuel or chemicals in circumstances such as the following:

- When a tanker is delivering fuel and the delivery hose leaks, or the receiving tank is over-filled.
- When a worker is decanting a liquid from one container to another by hand.
- If a storage tank or pipe becomes corroded and leaks.
- Collision between a forklift truck, or other vehicle, and containers holding liquids.

There were around 3,000 spills of oil and fuel in 2012 that were reported to the UK Environment Agency[17].

Fire

Fire is a danger for any organisation. The first responsibility is to protect human life, but fire may result in hazardous materials being released into the environment.

Chemicals and plastics may catch fire and release toxic fumes.

Water from fire-fighting appliances may flush hazardous chemicals into the drainage system or local watercourse. This is what happened in the incident in Switzerland referred to earlier.

Flooding

Rising flood waters flowing across a site may wash hazardous materials onto adjacent land or into local watercourses.

Equipment failure

If pollution abatement equipment (see sections 2.2 and 2.3) breaks down or malfunctions, planned emissions and discharges may fail to meet regulatory standards. Failures in process plant may also create pollution.

Pump and valve failures are a common source of pollution incidents associated with sewage treatment.

Are oils, other fuels or other hazardous liquids stored on your site?

If so, how are they stored?

Do you think that they are stored safely?

HAZARDS ASSOCIATED WITH ENVIRONMENTAL INCIDENTS

Environmental incidents can cause pollution through the release of harmful materials into the atmosphere, watercourses or surrounding land.

Air pollution

Fires always produce smoke – how far it travels will depend on the size of the fire and prevailing wind conditions. Smoke always has the potential to be a nuisance to local residents. In the worst cases it may contain toxic gases or particles of toxic material which can be harmful to health. These toxins may also damage local wildlife habitats.

Water pollution

Spills of fuel and chemicals and contaminated firewater run-off can reach local streams and rivers, killing fish and other wildlife.

Land pollution

Hazardous liquids can penetrate the ground around a site, killing vegetation. If groundwater is present, contaminants may be transported significant distances and eventually reach streams and rivers, or possibly wells used for drinking water.

Dealing with environmental emergencies

EMERGENCY RESPONSE PLAN

Incidents can quickly get out of control unless effective action is taken as soon as possible. Many organisations have well-established plans in place to deal with fire and other health and safety emergencies. Planning for environmental emergencies follows the same principles:

- The most likely accident scenarios (e.g. fire, spillage) need to be identified and key responses planned.
- A designated individual(s) needs to take charge of any incident.
- Site plans, including the location of drains and emergency equipment, should be held centrally.
- An inventory of hazardous materials (including type, quantity and safety data sheets) and their locations should be readily available.
- Telephone numbers for gas, water and electricity suppliers and the environmental regulator should be held centrally.
- Methods for advising local residents, businesses and any other parties likely to be affected should be in place.

Large organisations may have an Emergency Control Centre located in a special building. A small organisation should have somewhere that provides a central point for:

- implementing the emergency response plan; and
- holding key information.

This might be the gatehouse or a senior manager's office. The location should be protected, as far as possible, from the effects of any likely incident, e.g. by being on the site perimeter.

Is there an emergency response plan at your place of work?

Does it cover any potential environmental emergencies?

MATERIALS AND EQUIPMENT TO DEAL WITH POLLUTION INCIDENTS

Most organisations are likely to have fire-fighting equipment available as part of their existing fire precautions. Apart from fire, the most likely environmental incident is loss of a hazardous liquid through leaks and spills. If hazardous liquids are stored on site, it is essential that spill kits are placed at key locations so that any spills can be contained as soon as possible. Spill kits typically contain:

- Chemical-resistant gloves and other appropriate personal protective equipment (PPE).
- Absorbent mats or granules for soaking up liquids.
- Cushions or socks to place across the path of spills to prevent them getting into nearby drains.
- Wipes.
- Shovels and bags to collect contaminated material for safe disposal.

Drain covers may also be kept where they can be quickly used to seal-off open drains and prevent contaminants getting into the drainage system.

TRAINING

Incidents and emergencies have a tendency to happen when they are least expected. Chaos can result unless people know exactly what they need to do in a given situation and how to use the emergency equipment available.

Training is therefore at the heart of any effective response to environmental emergencies. Who should be trained and what should the training cover? The principles are really no different from those for fire and other health and safety emergencies:

- Everyone on your site, whatever their role, needs to know that there is a procedure in place for emergencies. All workers should know how to raise the alarm (e.g. what alarm system is used, how to use it, who to report an incident to, etc.).
- Workers who may be involved in dealing with an incident such as a spill will need more in-depth training, e.g. in the use of spill kits.
- Senior workers who have a co-ordinating role need to be trained in specific scenarios, so that the key decisions they make are as effective as possible.

- Contractors also need to be trained, especially if they are working in isolation on part of the site.

Appropriate training methods will vary depending on roles and responsibilities. General awareness about environmental emergencies could be included in induction training. Training for workers who are most likely to be involved in incident control might include:

- deciding whether an incident is minor or has the potential to cause major problems;
- practical training on how and when to use control equipment;
- desk-top exercises to work through likely scenarios; and
- emergency drills.

COMMUNICATIONS

Contacting the emergency services (fire, ambulance and police) is likely to be a first priority in the event of a major emergency, especially where people's health is threatened. For larger organisations, especially those operating potentially hazardous processes, it is good practice to establish regular contact with the emergency services. They will then be aware, in advance, of the conditions they are likely to encounter on site. Local residents will also need to be kept informed about any incidents that might affect them. The emergency services are likely to be involved in this, especially if any evacuation is required.

If there is the potential for a pollution incident, e.g. a spill of chemicals, to reach a local watercourse, there is a responsibility to inform the environmental regulator as soon as possible. The relevant contact details should be included in the emergency plan.

Environmental emergencies that cause pollution incidents, e.g. the death of fish in the local river, will attract attention from the media. Large organisations may be used to dealing with the media and employ communication specialists for this. For smaller organisations, media scrutiny may be an unwelcome shock. Bad media coverage can also damage any organisation's good name and reputation. All emergency plans should therefore cover how media contact will be dealt with. As a minimum this should include:

- Identification of one or two senior workers who will handle all media communications.
- Ensuring that other workers do not speak to the media and that they direct enquiries to the right person.
- Providing the nominated workers with appropriate media training.

Go back to the ideas that you wrote down in section 2.1 of this element.

Have your thoughts about the environmental impacts of your organisation changed at all?

Practice Question

PRACTICE QUESTION

Q7 Which of the following statements is true?

A Accidental oil spills are a significant source of water pollution.

B Emergency plans are only required for large organisations.

C Following an environmental incident all workers should be encouraged to speak freely to the press.

D The person who first raises the alarm should take charge of any environmental incident.

References

REFERENCES

1 BP Statistical Review of World Energy, http://www.bp.com/en/global/corporate/about-bp/statistical-review-of-world-energy-2013.html

2 http://www.bhopal.org/

3 http://www.metoffice.gov.uk/education/teens/case-studies/great-smog

4 http://www.who.int/phe/health_topics/outdoorair/databases/air_quality/en/

5 The World Environment 1972-1992, UNEP, 1992

6 http://ozone.unep.org/new_site/en/montreal_protocol.php

7 Sewage Treatment in the UK, Department for Environment, Food and Rural Affairs (DEFRA), 2002

8 http://www.coca-cola.co.uk/environment/water-conservation-reducing-our-water-use.html

9 http://www.eea.europa.eu/soer/countries/uk/soertopic_view?topic=waste

10 http://www.environment-agency.gov.uk/business/topics/waste/32200.aspx

11 http://www.worldbank.org/en/news/feature/2012/06/06/report-shows-alarming-rise-in-amount-costs-of-garbage

12 http://www.guardian.co.uk/sustainability

13 http://ec.europa.eu/environment/waste/

14 http://epp.eurostat.ec.europa.eu/statistics_explained/

15 http://www.unilever.co.uk/sustainable-living/wasteandpackaging/index.aspx

16 http://toxipedia.org/display/toxipedia/Rhine+Valley

17 http://www.environment-agency.gov.uk/research/library/position/41233.aspx

Notes